G. S. Craig

h. 138.

# THE CHANGING UNIVERSE

OTHER BOOKS BY JOHN PFEIFFER

*Science in Your Life*

*The Human Brain*

# THE
# CHANGING
# UNIVERSE

The Story
of the
New Astronomy

## by JOHN PFEIFFER

*With a Foreword by*
BART J. BOK
*Professor of Astronomy, Harvard University*

Random House, New York

*Drawings by Sol Ehrlich*

# FOREWORD

Radio astronomy is a young but vigorous science, which for a variety of reasons has not received the public attention it deserves. For some time now there has been a need for a good popular book on the subject. Unfortunately, there are few people who can really write such a book. Among the specialists, the astronomer is likely to shrink from becoming involved because he is thoroughly aware of his ignorance of advanced electronics, and the electronic physicist and engineer are similarly scared away because of their professed ignorance of astronomical facts. The intelligent, interested layman has been left looking for guidance and information, which, alas, were not readily available. It has become obvious that the Samuel Johnson which is radio astronomy needs its Boswell to make the new science better known, and John Pfeiffer deserves to become known as the Boswell of radio astronomy.

Two successive Guggenheim fellowships have enabled Mr. Pfeiffer to become well acquainted with the new science. He has had the time to sit down with almost every radio astronomer of note at home in the United States and abroad in England, Holland and France; he has talked with each of them about their special fields of research and their accomplishments as well as their hopes and fears for the future. He has developed an extensive correspondence with the radio astronomers he could not visit in person—those in Australia, for example—and by letter he has kept up to date with the latest progress at key places. Out of this effort has come the present book, which represents the first comprehensive popular survey of the field of radio astronomy.

Do not be misled by the apparent easy flow of John Pfeiffer's vivid prose, for in the actual writing he has profited by the experience gained during twenty years of science writing. The charm of this book rests in part upon the fact that he has checked and double-checked, written and rewritten, and that in the end he has produced a thoroughly competent and yet readable survey of a new and intricate field of science. I am glad that he has asked me to write a brief preface to *The Changing Universe*, since this gives me an opportunity to wish success to the latest Pfeiffer book and to thank the author on behalf of all radio astronomers.

Bart J. Bok
Professor of Astronomy
Harvard University

# ACKNOWLEDGMENTS

This book is the result of visits to laboratories in England and Holland as well as the United States. Most of the investigators whose studies are described have contributed directly to the book. They conducted me through their laboratories, explained their findings and described plans for the future. In many cases they also checked preliminary drafts of various chapters for accuracy in fact and in emphasis.

Among scientists in the United States, I am particularly indebted to Bart Bok, of the Harvard College Observatory, the first professional astronomer in the country to take an active part in the new science. He furnished invaluable advice and guidance, as did his colleagues Harlow Shapley and Harold Ewen. Other American investigators who gave generously of their time were John Hagen, Fred Haddock, Edward Lilley and Edward McLain, of the Naval Research Laboratory, in Washington, D.C.; Grote Reber, of Wheaton, Illinois; John Kraus, of Ohio State University; Harald Friis, of the Bell Telephone Laboratories; Jesse Greenstein and Walter Baade, of the Mount Wilson and Palomar observatories; Martin Schwarzschild and Lyman Spitzer, Jr., of the Princeton University Observatory;

Helen Dodson, of the McMath-Hulbert Observatory, in Michigan; and Bernard Burke, Lawrence Helfer and Merle Tuve, of the Department of Terrestrial Magnetism at the Carnegie Institution of Washington.

The story of the founder of the new science, Karl Jansky, who died in 1950, was prepared with the help of members of the Jansky family. They answered numerous questions and sent me several interesting excerpts from letters. Information about the support of radio astronomy in the United States was obtained from Alan Waterman and Raymond Seeger, of the National Science Foundation, which is playing an increasingly important role in promoting basic research in many fields. Charles Schauer, of the Research Corporation, and Richard Emberson, of Associated Universities, Inc., supplied material along similar lines.

Most of the chapters could not have been written without first-hand knowledge of work under way at foreign laboratories. The scientists I consulted in England include: Martin Ryle, Anthony Hewish and Fred Hoyle, of Cambridge University; Hanbury Brown, John Davies and Bernard Lovell, of the University of Manchester; and Stanley Hey, of the Radar Research Establishment. In Holland: Hendrik van de Hulst and Jan Oort, of the University of Leiden Observatory. In Canada: Peter Millman, of the Dominion Observatory, and Donald McKinley, of the National Research Council. Unfortunately, I was unable to visit one of the world's top-ranking radio observatories, the Radiophysics Laboratory in Australia. But I owe a great deal to my interviews with Bernard Mills when he was visiting this country, and to correspondence from Edward Bowen and Joseph Pawsey.

This is only a partial list. More than fifty other investigators discussed their research and plans with me. On the editorial side, I have many reasons to thank Hiram Haydn, of Random House. For one thing, the general subject of this book developed from talks with him. Also, his criticisms of chapters in their early versions have helped my writing enormously.

A fellowship from the John Simon Guggenheim Memorial Foundation—and encouraging conversations now and then with Henry Allen Moe, its director—made the book possible.

# CONTENTS

# ILLUSTRATIONS

THE CHANGING UNIVERSE

Aid of radio a gufumia

# INTRODUCTION

Little more than a generation ago a new science was born in the United States. It grew slowly and inconspicuously until just after World War II. Then, as demobilized investigators found themselves free to pursue research not immediately connected with winning a war, there came a period of astonishingly rapid progress. We are living in the midst of that period. Important advances have followed one after the other, and even more significant developments are imminent.

The new science is called radio astronomy. As the name implies, astronomers are scanning the heavens for the first time with the aid of radio equipment. Instead of observing light waves through telescopes they are listening to radio waves from the depths of space. They are learning from and working closely with experts in the art of designing aerials and vacuum tubes. The latest and most sensitive techniques of modern electronics, techniques originally created for radar and television and transoceanic communications, are being applied to a field of science whose beginnings date back to ancient times.

We have found a new universe, a rich and unsuspected

source of discoveries and of stubborn problems and mysteries. This may be one reason why radio astronomy has excited a large number of scientists as well as laymen, since there are fewer and fewer new places to explore on earth—only some jungles and mountain peaks and the polar regions. Exploration nowadays means looking up and beyond. We speak of visiting planets, and some day we may travel past our solar system. So stargazing has a new significance, a new thrill, in addition to its old and eternal fascination. The objects in our skies are not quite so remote as they once were. After all, we are looking at regions which future generations may know as well as we know the land around our homes.

The universe revealed by radio astronomy is a frontier in the twentieth-century sense. It must be explored at a distance, to be sure, but that is not an insurmountable handicap at this stage of our knowledge. We can observe places too far off to reach. We can even make maps of their general features, although the results are likely to prove as crude as the first efforts to chart a new continent. Radio astronomers have revealed entirely new facts about many familiar celestial objects. More than that, they have already found strange formations in the skies, some of which cannot be detected with optical telescopes. Just as intriguing are those whose existence is known or suspected because of circumstantial evidence, and which are waiting to be found with more advanced techniques.

Science is a thing of continual surprises and challenges. Not long ago astronomers had settled down to a relatively straightforward probing of the universe. Of course, there were new ways of detecting and measuring light and a large number of major problems to be solved, but the astronomers expected to approach the solutions along familiar lines, using reasonably familiar equipment. Now they are experiencing a revolution whose leaders have been newcomers to astronomy—physicists, radio engineers, specialists in electronics. A unique kind of observatory, the radio observatory, is taking its place among the world's astronomical stations.

This book tells the story of the new astronomy. It describes the research of the first investigators in the field, men who pioneered in work that is attracting more and more attention today. It also describes the kinds of unusual formations observed and identified so far, and the research which made such advances possible. Recent findings are being put to use, too, in military and peacetime applications which could not have been predicted even a few years ago. But the predominant aim of radio astronomy is to explore to the limit of our abilities a new universe of radio signals and radio objects, and to learn from remote events the secrets of our own origins and future.

# 1

BROADCASTS FROM SPACE

Twenty-five years ago an experimental radio aerial was built on what had once been a potato farm in Holmdel, New Jersey, seven miles from Sandy Hook Bay. The long, narrow structure consisted of brass-pipe frames mounted on a wooden scaffolding. It measured about a hundred feet from one end to the other, and looked somewhat like the skeleton of a giant airplane wing. Driven by a motor at the center, it rotated slowly on four wheels taken from a scrapped Model-T Ford. It was called the merry-go-round.

The man who built this aerial was Karl Jansky, a twenty-three-year-old radio engineer at the Holmdel station of the Bell Telephone Laboratories. Jansky, the grandson of Czech immigrants who came to the United States in a sailing vessel, was not hired to do pure research, and his aerial was no trailblazer. Similar aerials had been assembled before. This one was a solid, practical instrument constructed for solid, practical purposes, and every detail of the electronic circuits met some specific requirement dictated by those purposes.

Static was interfering with transatlantic and ship-to-shore radio communications. Recent advances had brought the art of receiver design to a fine point, and investigators of all nations were learning new facts about the causes of radio noise. Disturbances high in the earth's atmosphere could cause trouble. So could passing aircraft, and this observation was soon to be classified top secret and to serve as the basis for the invention of radar. Jansky's merry-go-round was designed to learn more about known sources of static, and that was exactly what it achieved. But it also happened to do something it was not supposed to do. The result was the new science of radio astronomy.

## FAINT HISSES

The young engineer was just out of college and this was his first job. Since he suffered from a chronic kidney disease and was under doctor's orders to live in the country, he was assigned to the Holmdel laboratory. During 1931 his aerial started scanning the skies methodically, rotating completely every twenty minutes in search of static. And static came from all directions. Jansky had little difficulty in identifying two sources. "Crash" static, bursts of crackling noise, came from local squalls and thunderstorms. Distant storms up to 140 miles away also produced definite effects.

But the nature of a third source baffled him completely. A type of radio noise never before detected was coming from some unknown place, and Jansky listened in at all hours, earphones clamped to his head. He described what he heard as, "Very weak . . . very steady, causing a hiss in the phones that can hardly be distinguished from the hiss caused by set noise." The hissing sometimes came in a bit louder than the familiar set noise—the extremely faint static which is inherent in every electronic circuit and is heard in every radio receiver—and sometimes faded out entirely.

That was all Jansky had to go on, the only clue to a new phenomenon and to a new branch of research. Under similar circumstances ninety-nine out of a hundred radio engineers would probably have paid little attention to the hissing, because there was no reason to expect it to be of practical importance. Yet Jansky's curiosity was aroused. Quietly, and at first quite unimaginatively, he started to track down the peculiar noise.

We read a good deal about hunches that pay off with brilliant and dramatic successes. Jansky had no hunches. During the course of his research he tested several theories about the cause of the noise, and not one of them checked with the facts obtained by the merry-go-round. In the beginning he looked for some fixed source of trouble, such as interference from local power lines or radio transmitters. This theory had a short life. The source, whatever its nature, did not stay put.

Then what sort of moving source could produce the hisses? A logical first guess would have been electrical storms, but that theory also failed to fit the facts. Storms appear in helter-skelter fashion, wherever atmospheric conditions happen to favor their formation. As any good weatherman will tell you, their ways are often highly eccentric; they may swerve with little warning and ruin carefully compiled forecasts. Jansky was receiving static from a source that moved regularly. Its path through the skies was predictable over long periods of time, which pretty much ruled out events in the earth's atmosphere.

In fact, the source seemed to coincide with the position of the sun. Day after day it rose in the east and set in the west, at about the same time as the sun. But more precise analysis eliminated the sun from the list of possible sources. Studies of hundreds of feet of charts showed that each day the source appeared at a position just a bit further ahead of the sun's position. It was slowly and steadily gaining on the sun. Every day it rose about four minutes earlier; every month it gained two hours. By the time a year had passed, the gain amounted to a full day—and the source was located in the same spot it had occupied twelve months before.

To account for these facts Jansky realized that he would have to study astronomy, and he found what he wanted in the early chapters of elementary textbooks. To us, the stars seem to move as if they were fastened to the inner surface of a rotating celestial sphere whose center is the earth, and star-gazers know that stars and constellations rise earlier every night, about four minutes earlier. A star which rises at

10:00 P.M. tonight will appear at 9:56 P.M. tomorrow night. The mysterious source of static was moving according to this timetable. It was rotating with the celestial sphere. Jansky also found that it lay in the direction of the constellation Sagittarius, the Archer. He suspected that the static was not coming from the constellation or star cluster itself, but from far beyond it in the same direction—presumably from the very center of our galaxy, the Milky Way.

Before Jansky announced his findings he decided to check back on some of his old records, just to be sure. But something seemed to be wrong. For a few days he examined and re-examined his charts, and he began to think he might have to discard his interpretation. The source of the static as recorded in early experiments did not move strictly according to the celestial-sphere schedule. Then with great relief he remembered one detail that explained everything. Those experiments had been conducted during the summer, when daylight-saving time was in force. A simple one-hour correction was sufficient to bring old results in line with new, and by the spring of 1932 he had established a clear-cut case for the existence of radio noise generated by a source in the direction of the center of the Milky Way—presumably the center itself—which astronomers estimate is about 26,000 light-years from the earth. Since a light-year is 6,000,000,000,000 miles, the distance is about 156,000,000,000,000,000 miles.

The merry-go-round, designed for entirely different purposes, had become the first radio telescope. Jansky had systematically ruled out theory after theory in his search for most probable explanations. The truth turned out to be the most improbable, the most fantastic, explanation of all. The hissing heard in the earphones could not be traced to local interference or to the upper atmosphere. It had nothing to do with the earth. Places beyond the earth, beyond the sun, beyond the remotest planets and the solar system itself, were generating static that sometimes annoyed businessmen, editors and diplomats engaged in overseas telephone conversations. The signals came from the depths of the Milky Way, from the stars and the wide spaces between them.

Scientific advances often come from those who are not seeking, but merely observing. When Jansky made his discovery, he was looking for something else, and other investigators be-fore him who deliberately sought radio signals from space had failed in their attempts. During the 1890's Sir Oliver Lodge, a British physicist best remembered for his ventures into psy-chical research, set up an apparatus near Liverpool and tried to detect radio waves from the sun. But, "There were evidently too many sources of disturbance in a city like Liverpool to make the experiment feasible . . . It might possibly be suc-cessful in some isolated country place. But clearly the arrange-ment must be highly sensitive in order to succeed."

Nearly four decades later, a year or two before the Holmdel experiments, another investigator came extremely close to making the crucial discovery. Unexplained static was recorded in Manila at a station run by the Radio Corporation of America. A young radio engineer named Gordon Stagner ob-served a hissing noise which was much louder at certain times of the day than at other times. At this stage, however, he was told to stop wasting his time and stick to his job. Stagner had no chance to analyze his records or continue the studies, and did not realize what he had found.

## A RADIO WINDOW

Today we can look back at Jansky's discovery and appreciate some of its most important implications. As the result of a single sudden and unexpected development, astronomy has found a new universe which may well prove to be vaster and richer than the one we knew. It is as if we had spent years slashing our way inch by inch through a dense forest, and all at once broke into the clear and saw before us a great plain reaching and disappearing into the remote horizon. Radio as-tronomy is revelation at the scientific level. It has become pos-sible to observe aspects of the cosmos which had been shut off from us by an apparently impenetrable barrier.

The earth is bathed in steady streams of radiation. Rays or waves of all sorts flow toward it from all directions—from the sun, the planets, nebulae (huge clouds of glowing gas), stars and the great aggregations of stars called galaxies. Some of the waves are too weak to be detected, others are enormously powerful. They are whispers and shouts from the universe, messages of a subtle and elusive kind which contain information concerning the nature of things. We would understand what is going on in space far better if we knew how to receive and decode a larger proportion of them.

The messages are produced by restless atomic particles. An electron revolving about the nucleus of an atom may suddenly jump back and forth from one position to another, and such jumps create pulses of energy, disturbances in space known as electromagnetic waves. All the radiation from space is produced by oscillating bodies, but the particular type of radiation depends on the rate of oscillation. The same general principle applies to the different notes on the piano. Striking the extreme left-hand key produces sound waves of very low pitch, because the sharp rap of a little hammer has set the proper string vibrating slowly. High notes are produced by strings which vibrate a good deal more rapidly.

Imagine another kind of piano, an instrument designed to set atomic particles vibrating instead of strings. Sitting at a mammoth keyboard, you reach over to press a "bass note" key at the lower end of the scale. No sounds are emitted, but atomic particles oscillate at a relatively slow rate, say, about ten thousand times a second. You are producing extremely long radio waves. Now you move your fingers from left to right along the scale, pressing successive keys. Each key causes atoms to vibrate more rapidly than the one before it, the "notes" are higher and higher. In order of increasingly rapid oscillations, the instrument creates shorter and shorter radio waves—those transmitted by radio stations, waves in the FM and television bands, and infrared heat waves.

But you have not exploited the powers of the electromagnetic piano. In fact, you have hardly reached the middle point of the scale, and an entire sequence of higher vibrations remains to be called forth. Strike the keys just to the right of the radio-infrared octave and you are "playing" the few electromagnetic waves that our eyes can detect—light waves, the colors of the rainbow from red to violet. Beyond the color keys, and there are only a few of them, come a great many keys which yield still higher waves—the ultraviolet rays that produce sun-tan and kill germs, X-rays, and gamma rays, the lethal radia-tions of nuclear weapons. The highest notes of all, the highest of all high C's, are represented by keys at the far right-hand end of the scale. These keys cause atoms to oscillate thousands of billions of times a second and fill the air with cosmic rays like those created in outer space.

Wonderful music could be composed if such an instrument existed. As a matter of fact, it does exist, but man did not make it and man does not play upon it. He is a part of it though, for the instrument is the universe.

Like ocean waves, electromagnetic radiations vary from great rollers to the tiniest ripples. Radiations resulting from the slowest oscillations have the longest wave lengths, that is, they measure the furthest from crest to crest. The most rapidly oscillating particles create radiations of extremely short wave length. The full range of radiations includes waves measuring from more than twenty miles between crests to considerably less than a trillionth of an inch—and all types are continually rolling out toward all celestial objects, including the earth.

But a thick wall lies between us and the stars. The earth's atmosphere cuts off most radiation before it ever reaches our instruments. Nature's signals may travel millions or billions of light-years toward the surface of the earth, only to be muffled and garbled and lost during the last hundred miles or so, an infinitesimal fraction of the total journey. It is like send-ing a robot spaceship to Mars and having it explode about an inch above one of the Martian canals, just as it was going to land. Out of all the messages from space the vast major-ity never reach us. They are dead letters, and they represent an appallingly extravagant waste of information.

We may find some small consolation in the fact that the wall of atmosphere has a few chinks. The chinks are barely large enough so that, like boys viewing a ball game through a knot-hole, we can catch a few inadequate glimpses of action taking place in the widest of all arenas, but they keep the wall from being completely effective. Some of the waves from space do get through. One opening lets in a trickle of visible light and some infrared and ultraviolet rays, radiation which represents an extremely narrow band of wave lengths, from about one-thousandth to one hundred-thousandth of an inch, a single octave of our mammoth electromagnetic keyboard. This chink in the wall has been called 'a "window" to the universe, but it hardly deserves to be called a window. It is more like the sort of slit found in the dark, gloomy towers of medieval castles. Yet it is all we had to look through before the coming of radio astronomy.

Jansky found a new window to the universe, a window really worthy of the name. Below the point where radiations with wave lengths up to a hundred-thousandth of an inch or so can pass through the old slit, there is a sharp cut-off. Longer waves are absorbed by oxygen and water molecules some fifty miles above the surface of the earth. The new window opens further along toward the lower end of the spectrum, where some waves a tenth of an inch long start to penetrate the barrier. It extends to waves about thirty yards long, at which point there is another cut-off, because longer waves bounce back off the top of the earth's atmosphere.

The radio window is not perfectly transparent. It has some dark places in it among the shorter wave lengths. For example, half-inch waves do not get through. These waves are absorbed by water vapor, a fact which radar engineers discovered during World War II. They built experimental radar sets using the half-inch waves and expected to spot enemy airplanes and warships more accurately at greater distances. The United States Navy installed the sets on ships of its Pacific fleet, only to find that they were receiving poor images. Water vapor can block military communications as effectively as signals from space.

But this is only a minor problem to radio astronomers, and the new radio window is more than a hundred times wider than the one used in conventional astronomy. We have been shut up in a dungeon for centuries. Now we are in broad daylight. No wonder astronomers are a bit dazzled by the prospect. "The thrill we feel is akin to that of Balboa first sighting the Pacific Ocean . . ." comments Bart Bok of the Harvard College Observatory. "We are just now becoming aware of the vast yet unexplored body of data which awaits detection, measurement and analysis."

## THE FIRST RADIO ASTRONOMER

Perhaps Jansky sensed the significance of his discovery, but not many others did. At first he may have expected a prompt and rapid increase in radio observations at many laboratories, because his work was widely reported. The public-relations staff of the Bell Telephone Laboratories, as wide-awake then as it is now, prepared and distributed an official press release, and the story was a natural for the nation's science writers. The May 5, 1933, edition of the New York *Times* carried a front-page, full-column report headed, NEW RADIO WAVES TRACED TO CENTER OF MILKY WAY. Similar reports appeared in newspapers and magazines throughout the country.

Within two weeks after the *Times* story, WJZ and the Blue Network featured a special evening program in which radio astronomy went on the air for the first time. Radio waves from the stars were picked up by Jansky's aerial, relayed to New York, and rebroadcast for the benefit of a national audience. A commentator described what was about to happen:

"You have taken part in some long-distance broadcast pick-ups—from across the continent, from Europe and from Australia. But tonight we plan to have a broadcast pick-up from further off than any of these, a pick-up that will break all records for long distances. We shall let the radio audience hear radio impulses picked up *from somewhere outside the solar system, from somewhere among the stars.* . . .

"In a moment I want you to hear for yourself this radio hiss from the depths of the universe. . . . Now, through the courtesy of the Long Lines Department of the American Telephone and Telegraph Company, I will let you listen in on the sensitive receiving set at Holmdel, fifty miles southwest of New York City. Mixed in with static you will now hear, will be the hiss of radio waves from the stars."

Then listeners heard the promised hiss, ten seconds of it. According to one reporter, "it sounded like steam escaping from a radiator." A short announcement was followed by another ten seconds of hissing. The stars were allotted a third and final ten seconds later in the program, and the commentator had a good deal more to say. Jansky was also heard, briefly. The program ended with the advice that antennas must be kept in first-class condition "if you are to get the full benefit of the wonderful programs on the air."

Millions of people learned for the first time that radio waves were coming from regions in extraterrestrial space. The news inspired a good deal of serious discussion, as well as the inevitable collection of crackpot letters, in some of which Jansky was reprimanded for missing the "really significant" point of his research—intelligent beings, living somewhere in the Milky Way, were trying to communicate with us. A woman who signed herself "Queen of the Universe" believed that the Bell Laboratories had made contact with wandering spirits of the dead. Some letters contained warnings that it was dangerous to probe too deeply into the nature of things, because that might upset the delicate balance of the cosmos. "Jansky received dozens of letters like that," a colleague told me. "There must have been four or five a week, and the mail from California was particularly heavy."

Jansky was only twenty-eight years old in 1933, and there was a great deal more research to be done. But he soon dropped out of the headlines. In fact, he was to spend very little time doing research in the field he had created. Four years later he made a few observations, tuning in on Milky Way static and noting that the longer the radio waves received, the stronger the signals were—a finding of major significance in present-day research. He also speculated about the possible origin of the static in hot interstellar gases. That was all. Jansky never again conducted experiments in radio astronomy. The remarkable thing is that he accomplished so much in so brief a period. He had spent only about a year doing intensive work on static from the stars, and that was on a half-time basis.

Rarely in the history of science has a pioneer stopped his work completely, at the very point where it was beginning to get exciting. Yet Jansky did just that, and I visited the Holmdel laboratory primarily to find out why. According to one explanation, he was simply not interested in the stars. As an engineer, he expected to stay with a problem as long as it proved of practical importance and no longer. He had detected a new type of static, discovered where it came from, and considered it merely one of many effects that had to be allowed for in designing more efficient radiotelephones.

"When the excitement died down, we thought things over," comments a radio engineer who worked with Jansky for many years. "We decided that there was no reason to go further. The noise figure for space had been established; we knew how much static to expect. We are working for a public utility and our purpose is to improve telephone services. We decided that the research should be done somewhere else, at universities or in government laboratories. Of course, if Karl had wanted to, he could have kept up his work. But I think he agreed with the decision. He didn't regret it."

But there is another side to the story. Jansky used to correspond regularly with his father, who had been an electrical engineer at the University of Oklahoma, and excerpts from some of his letters indicate that he was not at all happy about leaving radio astronomy. For several years he did all he could to convince his associates and superiors that the work was worth pursuing for practical reasons. But his arguments failed to produce results. Perhaps Jansky himself was not convinced by them. More than anything else, he may simply have wanted to explore the new field for its own sake.

A letter written in the spring of 1936 is particularly revealing. At that time Jansky wanted to leave his position. He thought of working at the State University of Iowa—but only if he was given freedom to go ahead with his studies in radio astronomy: "Of course, I would ask for the time and facilities to carry on my research, which would be more than I have had for the last two years." Jansky never made the move. He remained at the Bell Laboratories.

Once he hoped to build a huge dish-shaped aerial, perhaps a hundred feet in diameter, for studies at short wave lengths. The plan was submitted to the company's accountants, among other persons, who advised against it on the grounds of unjustifiable expenses. When this project and others failed to materialize, Jansky reluctantly gave up trying to continue his explorations in outer space.

Jansky became "noise expert" at the Holmdel station.

Whenever static began to cause trouble, he was promptly called in for advice—whether the static came from storms, stars, motor boats or home diathermy machines. He built a variety of sensitive aerials and recorders to help trace interference from these and other sources. During World War II he worked under a special military contract and later received an Army-Navy citation for his work on radio direction finders, aerial systems used to determine the positions of enemy transmitters.

At work Jansky showed little interest in getting ahead or outshining his associates. His competitive spirit was expressed outside the laboratory. He played an excellent game of bridge, and played to win. He also played tennis, and at one time was ping-pong champion of Monmouth County.

Jansky did not behave like a sick man, but his old kidney ailment was steadily becoming worse. The most serious symptom was rising blood pressure and he had to pace himself carefully, avoid excitement and see doctors regularly. "This sickness was hanging over him all the time," recalls Dr. Harald Friis, a top-ranking radio engineer and Jansky's immediate superior for many years. "Karl knew he would not live long. He didn't talk about it much, to me or to anyone else, but he never forgot it either." He suffered a severe stroke in 1949 and died early the next year, at the age of forty-four.

## PATTERNS IN THE UNIVERSE

By that time radio astronomy had taken root. Investigators had built a variety of radio telescopes, special receivers designed for high sensitivity and sharp focusing power, and were beginning to sweep the skies for an entirely different kind of message from the universe. A large proportion of the signals they detected, and are detecting, conveyed new and significant information because the entire search was such a new one. We are only starting to look. The radio universe is, above all, a new universe.

A New Yorker suddenly brought to the jungles of Africa might undergo a similar experience, provided he were young or wise enough to appreciate it. All the things he knows so well and takes for granted—taxicabs and skyscrapers and subways and flashing neon lights—simply do not exist in the new environment. There are unfamiliar sights, sounds as difficult to comprehend as the languages of the natives, a barrage of alien sensations. The radio astronomer is also trying to make sense out of the strange messages he tunes in from the depths of space. In his efforts he has certain advantages over the conventional or optical astronomer, the investigator who observes with mirrors and lenses instead of aerials and vacuum tubes.

For one thing, radio astronomy is full-time astronomy. Records can be obtained twenty-four hours a day, not just during sufficiently clear nights. The stars are great balls of gas which shine by their own light—that is, light and other radiations are produced by the bodies themselves. (Planets like the earth—as well as their moons—also shine, but their light is reflected from the sun.) Our sun is a star, and you see no other stars in broad daylight because it is so near that it completely outshines them. But this effect is not observed in the radio skies, and signals come through in fine fashion at all times. The signals also come through in all sorts of weather, penetrating clouds and fog and smog. Radio telescopes do not have to be built on the tops of mountains, and there is no premium on locations with clear skies. Radio techniques have been developed with special enthusiasm in England, where notoriously bad weather has long handicapped observers using conventional telescopes.

Furthermore, we have reason to believe that the radio universe may be considerably larger than the universe as observed by visible light. The range of a modern radio telescope may even exceed by a wide margin that of the great 200-inch telescope on Mount Palomar in California. Receivers built to tune in on radio waves from among the stars are so sensitive, and some of the remote celestial sources broadcast so powerfully, that it is now possible to probe further than ever before into space. Such receivers are detecting radio sources which may be billions of light-years beyond the maximum range of the Palomar giant.

The radio universe, the universe as observed by radio waves, is a thing of breath-taking possibilities, especially compared to what we have seen through the old window. Certainly the window is a mere slit, a limited section of radiations which make up a fragment of the broad electromagnetic spectrum. Yet even through this tiny chink we have looked out on the cosmos and observed prospects grander than anything conceived in science fiction. Knowledge came slowly, however. Mistakes and misconceptions lasted for centuries, and some of them were not set right until recent years.

Wherever men look, they see patterns. That is partly the nature of their minds, the way the human brain works. Early observers saw shapes in the skies and named the constellations accordingly—the Archer, the Big Dipper, the Hunter, and so on. But broader and more inclusive symmetries are not revealed to the naked eye. To see such things we had to extend our natural senses by means of light-gathering devices. Before Galileo the observable universe contained some five thousand stars. The first telescopes showed about half a million stars, and present-day instruments can see billions.

During the late eighteenth century a new symmetry was discovered in the heavens. The British astronomer William Herschel focused his telescope on nearly seven hundred different regions of the sky and counted all the stars he could see in each region. He found that the visible stars were distributed so as to form a system shaped like a grindstone. The symmetry was not perfect, however. It was not an intact grindstone but a "cloven" grindstone, with a piece missing, a rift or wedge-shaped region between the Swan and Archer constellations which seemed to contain no stars. At that time there was no reason to suspect that the rift was an illusion, that a great smog of interstellar dust was obscuring millions of stars.

Herschel's model has undergone only a few minor alterations since the 1790's. But our notions about the universe that includes this grindstone, and about our position in it, have changed radically. As recently as three decades ago most astronomers believed that our sun had a special place among its fellow stars, that it was located at the center of the grindstone.

Their belief was based on direct observations. They looked at many parts of the sky, and wherever they looked one rule seemed to hold. Most of the stars were concentrated relatively near our sun. The concentration was less at somewhat greater

*Karl Jansky working on his merry-go-round, the first radio telescope.*

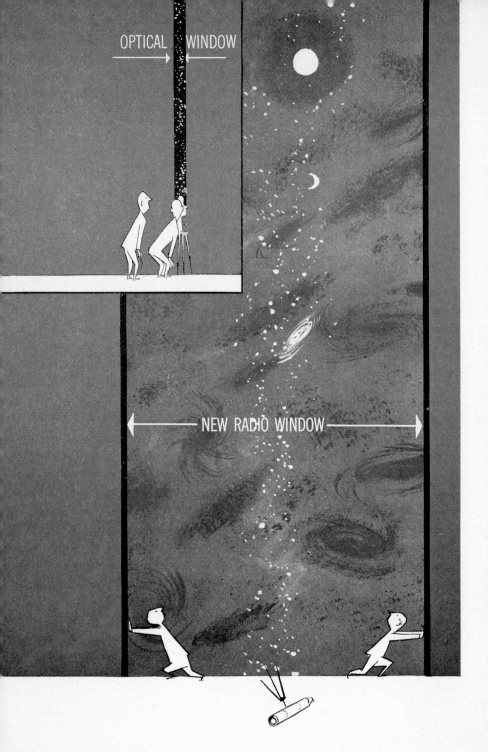

... *astronomy has found a new universe vaster and richer than the one we know* ...

distances, and still less in even more remote regions of space. In other words, the stars thinned out in all directions away from the sun. The outlying populations appeared to become less and less dense, like the suburbs and rural areas surrounding a large city. (This also turned out to be an illusion created by interstellar dust.)

To some people a universe with the sun at the center had a special appeal. The earth no longer held the central position. That was proved once and for all three centuries ago. But at least it might still be a member of a distinguished family, the solar system. The idea of our system enveloped in the heart of the cosmos like a precious egg in a nest had something reassuring, almost cosy, about it. It helped foster the feeling that in some way the universe had been designed for us, that we were the center of all things spiritually and physically. But evidence can be ruthless. In this case it showed quite definitely that there is nothing special about the sun. More than a generation ago Harlow Shapley of Harvard deduced that it is located thousands of light-years from the center of the grindstone, toward the outer rim.

An even more revolutionary discovery was made during the 1920's. Before then it was still possible to argue that the entire observed universe consisted of a single galaxy or star system, and that all the known nebulae and groups of stars lay within a radius of about 50,000 light-years from its center. That galaxy was the star system we see at night, our Milky Way. But in 1924, Edwin Hubble, looking through the optical window with the 100-inch Mount Wilson telescope, announced the discovery of the great spiral galaxy of Andromeda. This galaxy, the nearest spiral galaxy to our own and the only one we see with the naked eye, was nearly a million light-years away, far beyond the boundaries of the Milky Way.

That discovery extended our horizons enormously. It showed that the Milky Way was simply a local galaxy, and it led directly to our current conception of the universe, as an infinite expanse including hundreds of millions of galaxies, each of which contains billions of stars. The earth is recognized as a satellite of one of those stars, our sun. And the fact carries with it a significant implication, an implication that has become stronger and stronger during the last ten years. It seems likely that most stars, like the sun, have systems of planets and that plants and animals exist on many of the planets. Life is probably a widespread phenomenon in the universe. The odds are that somewhere among the galaxies scientists are developing atomic energy, spaceships and new methods of stargazing—including radio astronomy.

All these discoveries were made by peeking through the knothole that represents our optical window to space. Now we are starting to look at things through the much larger radio window. We are obtaining some first hints about what exists in the radio universe. And they are only hints. It would have been impossible to predict a universe of many galaxies from Galileo's observations of the moons of Jupiter, and as far as radio astronomy is concerned, we are in a similar position today. We have opened up new territories which call for centuries of new explorations.

# 2

## EXPLORING THE RADIO SKY

Jansky presented his final paper, a summary of his work up to that point, in April, 1937, at a Washington meeting of the Institute of Radio Engineers. Research almost stopped then and there, because, despite all the publicity about static from the universe, no group was yet ready to undertake full-scale studies. No one fully realized what had been discovered, and astronomers were busy with other problems. But at this stage an enthusiastic amateur, Grote Reber, of Wheaton, Illinois, stepped in and kept radio astronomy alive during its leanest years. In fact, he was already planning a new radio telescope, the first receiver designed specifically to study radio waves from space, when Jansky discussed his latest and last observations in Washington.

The Bell Laboratories engineer had found the new window to the universe, and circumstances permitted him to do little more. He had looked quickly through the window, in passing as it were, on his way to other and less exciting projects. He had seen signs of unusual activity and a fleeting image or two, but he found no time to stop. The experience was like that of a traveler passing through a lovely countryside and wanting to spend time there and hoping to come back some day, perhaps during a vacation. As a rule, unless you stop right away you never come back, and that is what happened in Jansky's case.

Reber found time to stop. He took a long and careful look through the new window, and saw many things which came as a complete surprise to astronomers and physicists. Receiving radio signals from the universe is hardly enough by itself. It raises a multitude of questions and provides no answers. We want to know where the signals are coming from, what objects emit radio waves of almost unbelievable intensity. And how are the radio waves produced? Their very existence is a sign of physical events which we are still trying to understand. Reber's work represents a pioneer effort toward the solution of such problems.

## NEW RADIO SOURCES

Reber became interested in radio astronomy as the result of a boyhood hobby. In 1927, at the age of fifteen, he was an ardent radio "ham." He made a receiver-transmitter set and spent his spare time communicating with other short-wave amateurs throughout the world. The walls of his room were covered with hundreds of "QSL" or recognition cards received from Czechoslovakia, the Union of South Africa, Peru and all parts of the United States.

About six years later, as a student at the Illinois Institute of Technology in nearby Chicago, Reber was still interested in long-distance radio. But terrestrial communications no longer offered a challenge, and he soon began thinking of new signals and more remote "contacts." What about bouncing radio waves off the face of the moon? First he built a ten-watt transmitter, but failed to pick up any signals. A transmitter four times more powerful also yielded negative results. Reber was more than ten years ahead of his time. It was not until after World War II that Signal Corps engineers, using far more advanced equipment, managed to send signals to the moon and catch them on the rebound.

The unsuccessful attempts, however, put Reber in the right frame of mind for what was to come. He was already looking toward the skies when he read Jansky's early papers. Here was something worth going into on a full-time schedule. The idea of listening in to radio waves from space, and interpreting the signals, excited the young investigator as no other idea had since he started building radio sets for himself at home. During the summer of 1937 he set to work on an ambitious construction project.

Neighbors stopped by to ask questions about the strange-looking structure taking form in his backyard. His blueprints called for a circular radio-wave reflector 31 feet 5 inches in diameter, made up of more than forty neatly fitted sections of galvanized sheet iron. This "pie plate" was to be fastened to the top of a bowl-shaped wooden framework which could be tilted toward different parts of the sky. Every piece of wood and sheet metal was pre-cut, numbered in advance, and ready to be put into place. The aerial, which somewhat resembled a giant parasol lying on its side, was completed in August.

Fifteen months and more than two thousand dollars later Reber detected his first signals from regions in outer space. At first he had tried looking at the universe through the short-wave part of the new radio window, which turned out to be a mistake. He used a receiver tuned to waves about three and a half inches long; then he went after thirteen-inch waves. Both sets failed to produce results. He did not realize it at the time, but signals at such short wave lengths were too weak for his equipment to pick up. Success came one October midnight in 1938, with a receiver for six-foot waves.

Reber adjusted his backyard telescope and dashed down to the cellar, where he had a crude meter. Like the temperature gauge on an electric oven, it consisted merely of a scale and a needle. That midnight the needle began to move slowly, indicating the passage of a strong source of static across the line-of-sight of the pie-plate aerial. Reber put on a pair of earphones to listen to the signals which the meter showed. He adjusted the volume control, tuned in on this remote "station" and heard a steady hissing noise. He knew it was static coming from the Milky Way.

Reber plunged into a schedule that would rapidly have discouraged a less hardy investigator. He often sat up all night in his cellar, watching the movements of the meter needle and jotting down readings in a notebook. He recorded the readings every minute on the minute from midnight, when static from passing cars and other man-made interference was at a minimum, until six o'clock in the morning. Then he drove thirty miles to Chicago, where he earned his living by designing home-type receivers for a local radio company, and back again in the evening to perform more experiments. He did his sleeping after supper, until just before midnight.

Reber's painstaking work furnished the data for several significant findings. In the first place, it confirmed Jansky's reports —and confirmation was called for, because some investigators were not yet convinced that the merry-go-round had actually picked up cosmic static. The power of the radio objects, whatever they were, would have to be enormous to send signals over such distances. An editorial writer for a large Eastern newspaper consulted astronomers and presented their opinions as follows: "It is hard to believe. . . . We infer a transmitting station of such staggering dimensions and energy that even an astrophysicist would hesitate to set down the billions and billions of kilowatts that must be radiated to register on the earth even the feeble effects noted by Dr. Jansky." But Reber proved the inference correct.

An even greater surprise was in store. Reber discovered new "hot spots" in the radio skies. When his aerial was pointing toward certain regions of space, it detected extra-intense signals. The signals did not fade or fluctuate. They came in steadily, as indicated by the position of the meter needle. Such sources were located in the direction of constellations other than Sagittarius, where Jansky had found the first radio source—in Cygnus, the Swan; Canis Major, the Big Dog; Cassiopeia, a W-shaped group of stars opposite the Big Dipper from the Pole Star; Aquila, the Eagle; and other remote regions. Apparently space contained many natural broadcasting stations, and these stations were dominant features of the radio skies.

Reber went still further. He directed attention to one of the most fundamental mysteries of radio astronomy, the physical nature of radio sources. It was a distinct possibility that the static he had observed was simply another form of radiation coming from visible stars. If so, the phenomenon was interesting and worth looking into, but it did not seem particularly promising and was certainly no surprise. No flight of imagination was required to suggest that the stars emit the entire spectrum of electromagnetic waves. Although stellar radio waves had never been detected, they undoubtedly existed.

But Reber's studies became more and more interesting with every set of new observations. The radio waves were not coming from visible stars. When Reber tilted his telescope so that it pointed at the brightest stars in the heavens, he was unable to pick up any signals. As far as he could tell, visible stars were "silent" in the long-wave broadcasting band, and radio waves must be generated at other places. Cosmic static was not merely more of the same thing, static produced by the same old familiar objects. Many of the strongest signals came from starless regions, from places barren of objects visible to the most powerful optical telescopes.

To be sure, this is negative evidence. It says nothing about the sort of body that emits the radio signals. We can only suspect that the stars contribute at best a small proportion of the messages. But the implication of this notion is sensational. It means that the universe contains things never before observed. There are unique objects in the radio skies, objects whose light —if any—is too faint to see and which we can know only through their radio waves.

Reber prepared three papers on his findings during the early 1940's, and two of them appeared in the astronomers' leading research publication, the *Astrophysical Journal*, but, the time was still not ripe for the coming boom in radio astronomy.

## MYSTERIOUS SIGNALS

The new work managed to attract little attention in normal times. But quite unexpectedly, scientists found themselves forced to pay serious attention to cosmic static during some of the grimmest days of World War II. The air over battle areas was buzzing with radio signals—messages flashed in secret codes from military and diplomatic headquarters, bomber squadrons in flight, radar outposts and many other sources. Receiving these messages rapidly and distinctly became a matter of life and death. But every now and then signals from space streamed into the atmosphere and interfered with terrestrial radio traffic.

In 1944 the Nazis started sending V-1 buzz bombs into London. Anti-aircraft guns, directed by vacuum-tube computers or "electronic brains," were pressed into service and proved so accurate that they downed more than ninety percent of the flying bombs. But intelligence reports gave advance warning of a faster and considerably more dangerous weapon, the V-2 rocket. This missile required new countermeasures. Part of the plan called for the Royal Anti-Aircraft Command to develop radar equipment which would detect the giant rockets as soon as possible after they were launched from their camouflaged bases on the other side of the English Channel.

The job was assigned to Stanley Hey, one of the Command's best young scientists, who is now a leader of a British government radio-astronomy research group in Malvern. A specialist in crystal structure before the war, he had received rush training in electronics: "They tried to make a radio expert out of me in six weeks!" Within two months Hey had helped modify a standard radar set originally designed to aim guns, built a special array of aerials and produced an effective instrument to detect V-2 missiles. But one problem continued to cause trouble, particularly in sensitive long-range work when radar crews attempted to pick up weak signals bouncing back off distant rockets. These signals were sometimes lost as a louder noise interfered with clear reception. Hey says the interference consisted of radio waves from deep in our galaxy, the same sort of radiation studied by Jansky and Reber.

This experience and others like it proved far more effective in stimulating further studies than technical talks and articles. After the war radio astronomy gradually came into its own. It was recognized as a field that required considerable development, and groups of scientists soon went to work on a more ambitious scale. At first nearly all these investigators were former radar specialists from England and Australia, using souped-up radar apparatus to observe cosmic radio waves instead of enemy airplanes and battleships. Later, astronomers began to take notice and joined in new surveys of the radio skies. Radio astronomy became a full-fledged science with long-term projects, large grants to support them and large research teams.

In such a setting Reber continues to occupy a unique position. He is largely self-educated and his important contributions have been made strictly on his own, in laboratories he built himself and with equipment he designed and assembled. He likes to work alone, and is somewhat bitter when he recalls the early days when it was impossible to obtain funds for research. About three years ago a large conference was being organized in Washington and officials wanted Reber to attend. Here is part of a letter he wrote at the time to the Research Corporation in New York, the foundation that has helped support his recent studies:

I take a dim view of speech-making, compared to those who organize conventions. My reluctance to go to Washington is not merely the expenditure of several hundred dollars to make a twenty-minute talk, which does seem rather out of proportion. But travel is hard work and I'm not up to it now. . . . Jansky suffered from poor health, he talked without visible success.

As he explained to me one time, the electrical engineers were not interested because they didn't know any astronomy and couldn't find anything useful in the subject. The astronomers were not interested because they didn't know any electrical engineering and considered their present techniques adequate for the study of the Universe. . . .

It now appears that our savants have discovered radio astronomy through the efforts of the British and Australians. This bears out a statement by Kettering to the effect that the best way to get the inventions of the General Motors Laboratories into General Motors cars was for Chrysler or Ford to start using them.

After the war Reber had progressed to a point where his backyard would no longer do as an observation site. He was using more sensitive equipment now, and interference from increasing automobile traffic spoiled many of his records, even during after-midnight hours. So he started to look for funds and an out-of-the-way spot for his radio telescope. He tried the universities and half a dozen companies interested in electronics, and Karl Jansky put in a good word for him at the Bell Telephone Laboratories. Finally, in November, 1947, a leading Federal scientific agency, the National Bureau of Standards, in Washington, made him an offer after three of its investigators visited his cellar laboratory in Wheaton—and he took the job. This was his only official position at an electronics research laboratory.

He had an impressive title at the Bureau: Chief, Experimental Microwave Research Section. His pie-plate telescope was taken apart, sent East, and put back together again on an isolated field in nearby Virginia. Reber redesigned three larger radar aerials captured from the Nazis and painted red, white and blue to "Americanize" them. For nearly two and a half years things appeared to be working out reasonably well; at least, it seemed so to outsiders.

What was actually happening is a matter of opinion and some controversy. But Reber felt increasingly dissatisfied with the way his research was shaping up at the Bureau. One day in the spring of 1951 he left for a routine two-week vacation. He went West and kept going, and the next time his associates heard about him he was staying at the Maui Grand Hotel in Hawaii, more than 5,000 miles away.

Reber had started his research thirteen years before by trying to detect short-wave radiations. Now he was ready to observe through the other end of the radio window to space, and try tuning in on extremely long waves which had not been observed extensively. Since this work required a site above the clouds, he went in for mountain-climbing. He inspected the tops of Mauna Loa and Mauna Kea but finally chose another peak, 10,000-foot Haleakala, an extinct volcano on the island of Maui. This mountain was the easiest of the three to scale, because during the war the Army Signal Corps had completed a road to the top—single lane to the 6,000-foot level, double lane from there on up—where a military lookout was located. At first Reber intended to build the framework of his new radio telescope out of a native material, bamboo, but he finally settled for redwood: "All the giant bamboos, the ones suitable for construction work, were growing in Hawaiian botanical gardens."

Reber bought a second-hand truck to carry cement and other materials to the mountain top. He moved from the Maui Grand Hotel to a cottage some 3,500 feet up the slopes of Haleakala, "forty minutes from the top and forty minutes from the nearest town." His only neighbors were a few natives and ranchers, and no one was particularly curious about his project. A grant from the Research Corporation, and "two tough-looking Portuguese workers," helped him finish his radio telescope.

For about three years Reber battled continuously with some of the most intricate phenomena encountered in the new science. Although it is true that radio observations can be made twenty-four hours a day and in all kinds of weather, this general rule does not hold for the longest radio waves from space. In daylight, streams of particles emitted by the sun crash into the earth's atmosphere, knock the electrons off myriads of atoms and may produce electrical storms and other disturbances. The bombardment may cause such intense and widespread static that it interferes with the reception of long radio waves (short waves are less distorted as they pass through atmospheric storms). Being above the clouds, as Reber was, helps somewhat, but the best long-wave observations come after dark. Another problem, which hampers observation at all times, is that the longest waves that can be observed by radio techniques tend to bounce off the upper atmosphere and travel back into space.

The atmospheric static with which Reber and all radio astronomers have to contend may indirectly furnish useful information, although not about outer space. By studying interference effects which distort cosmic radio signals, investigators are learning new facts about the structure of the atmosphere. For example, certain peculiar radio records have led Reber to believe that there is "a great bulge in the outer parts of the earth's atmosphere, approximating a thick disk."

The long waves that do get through the atmosphere are extremely difficult to interpret. Looking through the new window to the universe, investigators see many relatively clear pictures—regions emitting sharp and intense signals—at medium and shorter wave lengths. Reber is not interested in studying these images. He is concentrating on the blurred and fragmentary images that appear in the radio skies and are often too complex to understand at all.

In Hawaii he first tried tuning in on radio waves from six to fifteen yards long. "Most of the results are unintelligible." At wave lengths of about three yards the situation was somewhat better. The records he obtained from intense radio sources are still in the process of being analyzed.

In 1954, Reber deserted the slopes of Haleakala for Tasmania, Australia. One of his projects was to investigate a theoretical "hole" in the ionosphere, the upper layers of the earth's atmosphere. This gap is produced by the effects of the earth's magnetic field in an atmospheric layer about three hundred miles above the surface. There were problems, as usual, including serious interference from power lines, but not long ago Reber achieved some important results. He is listening in on cosmic static at extra-long waves—about 150 yards—which is a significant enlargement of the new window to the universe. He wrote me from Tasmania last summer, "The cosmic static is very strong. The hole stays open nearly every night and closes with a snap at sunrise. I think I'll stay the rest of the winter!" If we can actually observe through this hole, we shall learn a great deal more about the nature of radio sources and the atmospheric disturbances which interfere with radio and television communications on earth.

Commenting on Reber's work, a leading radio astronomer summed up the opinion of many investigators: "Reber will be ahead of the game all the way. He's a real leader. Most of our laboratories couldn't keep up with him."

## RADIO OBSERVATORIES

Research is now being conducted at a dozen new laboratories which did not exist before World War II. England has two major radio observatories besides the one headed by Hey: the University of Manchester's Jodrell Bank Experimental Station, and a group at the Cavendish Laboratory of Cambridge University. The Jodrell Bank center is already competing with Stonehenge, the Tower of London and Loch Lomond as one of Great Britain's leading tourist attractions. It is the site of a mammoth radio telescope which looks like something that might appear on the cover of a science-fiction magazine. The large telescope at Cambridge is also a spectacular instrument, although it has not been so well publicized.

The Australian government has established a Radiophysics Laboratory in Sydney. This laboratory includes the world's largest group of professional radio astronomers and is the only place where large-scale studies of the southern skies are being made. A Dutch center at the University of Leiden Observatory is also carrying out an important program which was conceived and planned in secret during the Nazi occupation of Holland.

The leading American groups are at Ohio State University; the Naval Research Laboratory, in Washington; the Harvard College Observatory; and the Carnegie Institution of Washington. Investigators at these and other laboratories are listening in to cosmic static with a variety of special aerials—sophisticated descendants of Jansky's merry-go-round.

The large proportion of the workers at these new radio observatories who were once radar specialists had a postwar choice of continuing radar research, developing high-speed electronic calculating machines and television or going into radio astronomy. Many excellent scientists went into astronomy. Edward Bowen, founder of the Radiophysics Laboratory in Australia, was a leading radar expert during the war. American radar men remember him as the man who walked into a Massachusetts laboratory one day in 1940, carrying a new top-secret electronic tube in his pocket. More than any other single invention, this so-called magnetron gave us a lead in radar research which Germany and Japan were never able to overcome.

Bernard Lovell, director of the University of Manchester's station, helped develop radar bombsights which enabled the Royal Air Force to make precise hits on industrial targets through thousands of feet of fog. His brilliant colleague, R. Hanbury Brown, was one of the original 1936 group that invented radar. Other leaders who were active in radar research during World War II include Martin Ryle, head of the British laboratory at Cambridge University and John Hagen, who has established the special section at the Naval Research Laboratory in Washington.

Like these men, the great majority of radio astronomers are not astronomers by training, but they have made most of the discoveries that are changing and extending our ideas about space and the universe. At present they are engaged in an intense international race for new discoveries and new honors. Research is sometimes presented as a profession followed only by disinterested men and women, who care little for such things as priorities—who did what first—personal recognition and credit. No one who subscribes to this point of view should take radio astronomy as an example.

Of course, there is considerable free exchange of information. British and American investigators pooled their knowledge to identify one of the most intense radio sources ever discovered, and there are many other cases of close co-operation. But the competitive spirit also plays a major role in the field. Members of the high-powered Australian group, for instance, go after research projects with the same verve and gusto that characterized the soldier from Down Under during the war. According to one story, some time ago they chose a mountain peak near New Guinea as the site for a radio telescope. But the peak of another mountain was in the way, blocking off radio waves coming from parts of the sky near the horizon. Undiscouraged, they bought an ample supply of dynamite and blew off the top of the offending mountain.

I have not been able to confirm this story. In fact, a scientist who should know informs me that it was probably dreamed up one evening over a few tankards of ale. Still, it certainly indicates how vigorously the Australians tackle their problems, man-made as well as natural. They keep a careful eye on progress at British radio observatories and enjoy beating them to a new finding. British workers are equally competitive, and the United States is now beginning to enter into the spirit of things.

Until recently, however, the United States has been running an unspectacular third in the international race. Radio astronomy did not attract many American radar experts immediately after the war, and it is interesting to consider why it got off to a slow start in the country where the first discoveries were made. There is no simple explanation, but one of the reasons involves the problem of who is to support research when the universities and industry are not interested or cannot afford to pay the price. The Australian government backed radio astronomy early in the game; that is, shortly after the war. In England, government funds are supporting the work at Malvern and paying an appreciable part of the cost of the Jodrell Bank telescope. Today the American government, acting largely through the National Science Foundation, is aiding radio astronomy on an increasing scale. But the foundation is a relatively new organization, and our work would be further along if such help had been forthcoming years ago.

Dr. Vannevar Bush, president of the Carnegie Institution, has expressed the need for continued support of basic science: "Today it is truer than ever that basic research is the pacemaker of technological progress. In the nineteenth century Yankee mechanical ingenuity, building largely upon the basic discoveries of European scientists, could greatly advance the technical arts. Now the situation is different. A nation which depends upon others for its new basic scientific knowledge will be slow in its industrial progress and weak in its competitive position in world trade, regardless of its mechanical skill."

## THE RADIO SKIES

Radio techniques demand basic scientific knowledge in electronics as well as astronomy and physics, because we are in the process of building a different kind of synthetic sense organ. Microscopes, conventional telescopes, microphones which can amplify an ant's footsteps so that they sound like the thud of heavy boots—such instruments extend senses we already have. But radio telescopes are an example of devices which, in effect, endow us with new senses. As far as radio waves are concerned, we start almost from scratch, as if we had been born blind and were suddenly able to see for the first time. Astronomers use radio-telescope records to deduce the nature of events that would otherwise remain entirely unknown.

The new universe may be pictured by imagining what things might look like if we had radio vision. Our eyes are no longer sensitive to light waves but to the fuller range of radio waves, such as those used in short-wave radio, television and radar. This is a weird world. A typical landscape appears in richer, more varied colors because there are far more types of radiation to distinguish. You can make out the general shapes of trees, houses and other objects, particularly at the shorter "violet" wave lengths. But they are blurred, as if you were peering through water, and most of the details are lost. Sharp focusing is not possible.

You cannot distinguish the individual leaves of trees, for example. Conventional homes afford no privacy. You see through walls, because radio waves penetrate ordinary building materials easily (if this were not true, of course, station-to-home broadcasting would be impossible). Shielding consisting of wire mesh is used instead of walls, curtains and blinds. And you must think up new ways of recognizing your friends and acquaintances, since individual features do not show up clearly. Under certain conditions—say, when the intensity of radio "light" in a room is about the same as that coming from a person—people disappear entirely. They become radio ghosts and you can detect them only if they carry special vest-pocket radio transmitters whose signals identify them uniquely.

How would things beyond the earth appear to you? The skies viewed by radio light include many surprising features. You still see the sun as the biggest and brightest object, and it rises and sets according to its usual schedule. But there are amazing dawns and sunsets. Our familiar visible sun appears about as large as a penny held at arm's length, but the radio sun is something else again. It seems as large as a circus tent. Its area is much greater than that of the familiar sun, because strong radio waves come from the vast solar atmosphere or corona, which emits little light and is invisible to ordinary vision.

The radio sun is noteworthy for another reason. Since at longer wave lengths the signals we receive are more intense from outer portions of the corona than from inner portions, it does not appear as a disk of uniform brightness. It is brighter at the edges than at the center, forming a kind of celestial wheel with a glowing red rim and a somewhat fainter yellow hub. There is also a radio moon. It is about the same size as the moon we know (our satellite has no wave-emitting atmosphere), but a good deal dimmer. It moves through the skies, a pale radio version of the satellite we know, hardly a romantic object.

As for the stars we see at night, the situation is even stranger. Under good observing conditions our eyes can distinguish several thousand distinct stars—but not a single one of them appears in radio light. Although they are all almost certainly emitting radio waves, as our sun does, they are so much further away that their signals—which are weak in comparison to those of other sources—cannot be detected. The radio heavens do not contain an ample population of twinkling pinpoints of light. You would look in vain for the Pole Star, the Evening Star, the Big Dipper and other well-known landmarks of the night.

The radio sky is not empty, however. It contains numerous bodies, perhaps as numerous as the visible stars themselves. There is a Milky Way of a sort. Like the stars, many radio sources are concentrated about the flat central plane of our galaxy. But they tend to be the more powerful radio-wave emitters, and so the Milky Way is somewhat less milky and extends as an extra-bright belt of radio light. You see shining spots that mark intense broadcasting regions in space, bright streaks and drifting luminous blobs and wispy shifting shapes resembling bits of incandescent mist. For the radio universe, we have to rewrite our astronomical textbooks, and think up new constellations and new names for them.

This is a general picture of a universe we may never see directly, with our own eyes. Some people might say that it is a universe we were never meant to see. Certainly they have reason to be concerned, because what we are learning is already upsetting many notions about the nature of things. Indeed, science is a systematic method of upsetting notions and arriving at new ones which are, for a time, more plausible. There are undoubtedly a great many more radio objects than we know of today, and the theories discussed in this book may seem naïve a generation from now. But that is precisely the point of doing research. In science an idea that does not seem naïve after a hundred years is often suspect. It may well be a superstition rather than a hypothesis. The problem in the radio universe, as in the optical universe, is to discover which is which.

# 3

## TUNING IN ON THE STARS

The world's largest telescope is no longer the one located on the top of Palomar Mountain in California. It is a giant instrument set in the middle of a Cheshire cow pasture near the tiny English village of Lower Withington, the latest addition to the Jodrell Bank Experimental Station. If you can imagine the Empire State Building placed in an Iowa cornfield, you will have some idea of how this extraordinary structure impresses people seeing it for the first time. There is absolutely nothing in the surrounding countryside—or in the whole of Great Britain, for that matter—to compare with it.

Looming high in the air is a huge aerial, a mammoth version of the kind commonly used with radar sets. It is made of sheet steel shaped in the form of a bowl, a bowl large enough to hold a fleet of trucks. It is 250 feet in diameter, more than twice as big across as the dome of the Capitol in Washington. (For comparison, the reflecting mirror of the Palomar telescope measures a mere 200 inches in diameter.) Seen from a distance, the bowl seems to be a delicate thing hanging in space like the span of a great suspension bridge.

The illusion can be traced to beautiful designing. Actually

the bowl is massive and rugged. It weighs about five hundred tons and is supported at the ends by two towers eighteen stories high. The lowest parts of its foundation, more than a hundred and fifty reinforced-concrete piles, extend half as deep into the earth. The towers roll on locomotive-type wheels along a circular track so that the aerial can sweep around across the horizon like a lighthouse beacon. A huge gear-and-rack mechanism at the top of the towers tilts the aerial to any angle from the horizon line to the zenith of the sky. The mechanism was purchased from the British Navy and once moved the fifteen-inch guns of the battleship *Royal Sovereign*.

This is the largest electronic instrument ever constructed. It is nearly finished. Only the powerful driving motors must be put in place—and then the entire structure will be under precise push-button control. The control room has already been built, and it resembles a Hollywood setting for a world-of-tomorrow laboratory. The operator sits at an electronic console which looks something like the keyboard of a cathedral organ. On either side of him are control panels six feet high and filled with more dials and meters and switches than a B-52 bomber. He looks straight ahead, through a wall of glass, at the enormous radio receiver several hundred yards away.

When the motors are installed, the operator will be able to play on the electronic organ. He will press one combination of buttons and the bowl will move smoothly on oiled bearings to a pre-selected position, focusing on a radio source. Pressing another set of buttons will make the bowl follow the source on its path through the skies. The operator may want to do more than fix on a radio source and track it. He may want to scan it at the same time, to have the aerial move from side to side and up and down like a person reading a book. If so, he will only have to push further buttons and the controls will take over for hours at a stretch. The entire system will run by itself, a robot observer of the radio universe.

## THE UNIVERSE IN FOCUS

The "Big Dish" cost nearly $1,500,000 and represents seven years of planning and construction. Those seven years have been a fulfillment and a nightmare for Bernard Lovell, who conceived the project and played the chief role in seeing it through. His own research has been severely curtailed by the task of creating an instrument many times larger than any of its predecessors. He spent hours selling the idea, obtaining funds, explaining, persuading, lecturing, holding press conferences, facing innumerable delays and emergencies. At first no one was willing to do the construction job, or even to estimate its cost, but finally Lovell managed to find an engineering firm with enough imagination to undertake the work, Husband and Company in Sheffield.

The result is the most spectacular of the hundred and fifty-odd radio telescopes in existence today. These new instruments are the basic apparatus for the new astronomy. They are traps, highly specialized and selective traps, for radio waves from space. They gather and register a whole jumble of signals, many of which are unwanted. Terrestrial radio noise, natural and man-made, may come in from a thousand and one different sources. Storms and electrical machines and airplanes and tractors and radar sets make their contributions to the records. Even the telescope's own vacuum tubes produce persistent and troublesome noises.

And mixed in with it all, buried deep under an avalanche of static, are the feeble signals of the radio universe. The signals are messages from the Milky Way and from remote galaxies, streams of information which must be isolated from the universal hubbub. They must be extracted from stronger signals which do not interest us, amplified millions of times and recorded and preserved in permanent form. They are treasures of a most important kind, raw and undigested facts to be analyzed and transformed into the growing and exciting thing we call knowledge. Radio telescopes, the greatest contribution of electronics to the exploration of space, gather these facts for us.

Here is how the Big Dish works. Radio waves travel through space, penetrate the earth's atmosphere and reach the bowl of the telescope—an electronic mirror or reflector. The waves strike the bowl and bounce back toward a focal point, just as light rays do when they hit a properly shaped mirror made of glass or metal. Protruding straight out about sixty feet from the center of the bowl is a "half-wave dipole," a small metal-rod antenna resembling the type used for FM radio reception. The bowl is so shaped that the rebounding waves come together and strike the tip of the antenna.

The next stages resemble those which take place in any home radio or television set. When waves from a local broadcasting station strike your aerial, they produce small electrical currents which flow along the aerial wire into the vacuum-tube circuits of the set. The same thing happens in the Big Dish. Currents created in the aerial by radio waves from a radio source pass to the receiver, where they are amplified and fed to a recorder. As a rule, the recorder is an automatic-pen device. The source writes its "signature," a series of humps and jagged lines, on a strip of moving chart paper.

These are the elements of what happens, although things may not always work out that simply. Radio astronomers are continually refining their radio telescopes, designing new circuits to receive fainter and more remote broadcasts. Many problems remain to be solved, and one of the most important concerns "resolving power"—the ability of any observing device to distinguish between two close-together points at a distance. For example, presumably you have no trouble seeing the words of this sentence as you read. If you begin moving back from the book, however, the sides of each individual letter make a smaller and smaller angle with your eye until everything becomes blurred.

Under normal indoor lighting a person with perfect eyesight barely sees an object whose sides make an angle of about one minute of arc with the eye (one minute is a sixtieth of a degree, or 1/21,600 of a circle). This is perfect 20-20 vision. If you have it, you can try the following experiment on yourself. Draw an "O" (the actual size of this letter) on a blank piece of paper, have someone hold it up at eye level, and step back about ten feet. You should be able to make out the letter without undue trouble.

Using the Mount Palomar telescope, you could see the "O" at a distance of about six miles. In astronomical terms, if you look at the moon on a clear night you can distinguish an object seventy miles across, say, a large crater. The telescope obtains enormously greater detail at the 240,000-mile range, distinguishing lunar objects only about 125 feet from edge to edge.

As far as resolving power is concerned, radio telescopes cannot compete with the human eye, much less with the Palomar telescope. The focusing of an observing instrument depends on the wave length of the radiations being received. The longer the wave length, the larger the telescope needed—and radio waves are millions of times longer than light waves. A radio telescope designed to observe one-yard waves with "20-20 vision," the resolving power of the eyes, would have to have an aerial more than three miles in diameter. To match the Palomar telescope would require an aerial wider than the Pacific Ocean.

For some time to come radio telescopes will continue to provide rather "blurred" electronic images. But radio astronomers have made notable advances in their drive to obtain sharper focusing. Judged by modern standards, the merry-go-round aerial built by Jansky hardly rated as a high-precision instrument. It may be compared with one type of microphone which broadcasting engineers often use to receive sound waves. Such a microphone is fine when you want to pick up sounds from a large region, say, the clapping and hubbub of an entire studio audience. In engineering language it has a wide "cone of reception." But sometimes you want to hear the comments of a single person in the audience, or a small group of persons. That calls for a highly directional "narrow cone" microphone. This sort of device can be "aimed" at a selected spot. It picks up sounds coming from that spot, and is relatively deaf to sounds from nearby places.

Jansky's first aerial was a wide-cone instrument for detecting radio waves. At any given position it covered thirty-five degrees of sky, which means that it received radiation from an extremely broad region and could not pick up a small radio source. The source would be lost in the general noise produced by many sources. Today radio astronomers, taking advantage of new designs and equipment, are building instruments with relatively narrow reception angles or cones. The Big Dish, for example, covers a mere tenth of a degree of sky when it is receiving signals at the short-wave end of the radio spectrum.

This improvement, considerable as it is, does not solve all problems by itself. One radio source measures some thirty thousand light-years across. It is more than two hundred million light-years away, and at that distance the Big Dish receives radio waves from a region of sky about a million light-years across. In other words, its resolving power is not good enough to bring this source into sharp focus. New radio-telescope circuits have been built to give greater precision, many of which involve subtle applications of the electronic art. One of them is another outgrowth of World War II radar research.

Early in the war engineers experimented with "rocking-chair" radar, in which an aerial was mounted on a platform that tilted back and forth at a regular rate, a motor-driven see-saw. Its reception cone was considerably broader than the profile of a distant enemy plane, so it took two quick "looks" at the plane, one with the left edge of the reception cone, the other with the right edge. When the two images were equally intense, the target lay directly on the line between the two aerial positions.

This gadget effectively increased the resolving power of radar. Furthermore, the rocking chair itself turned out to be unnecessary. The same results can be obtained by eliminating the tilting platform and doing the whole thing electronically with a technique called lobe-switching. Radar sets incorporating the new technique spotted fighters and bombers about ten times more accurately than previous models and brought down two to three times as many planes. Radio telescopes equipped with even more sophisticated circuits achieve similar results in locating remote sources of interstellar static. Such circuits add to the precision gained by using bigger and bigger bowl-shaped aerials.

## TWIN AERIALS

Lovell's Big Dish represents one type of radio telescope. The leading exponent of another spectacularly successful type is Martin Ryle, who heads the British radio-astronomy group at

Cambridge University. Ryle and his associates work at Cavendish Laboratory, at a new yellow-brick building in the center of the "Rifle Range," a site used as a wartime training station. The range is a narrow strip of land more than two thousand feet long and running in an east-west line. It also includes two rectangular plots, one at each end of the strip. Horses and cows graze nearby in wooded farmland.

During a recent visit I walked along a footpath from the laboratory building in the center toward the west end of the range. First there was a searchlight-shaped aerial, a smaller version of the bowl of the Big Dish. Then I passed a long array of eighty antennas; below them in the grass was a sheet of wire netting used to reflect radio waves. Finally, at the end of the strip, I came to a silver-painted box made of cast iron and resembling a small kitchen oven. The box contained amplifiers for the giant instrument standing in the west rectangular plot of the range.

The instrument occupies an area about the size of a football field. It consists of eighteen radio towers lined up in two 300-foot parallel rows as neatly as soldiers on parade. Pivoted at the top of each tower is a slender curved structure, a supporting element whose ends extend to either side like metal arms reaching toward the sky. The eighteen unusual-looking towers serve as the framework for a great wire-net antenna which includes some twelve miles of wire, and is connected to the cast-iron box and the central laboratory by heavy cables. The elaborate equipment is the "Big Dish" of a different sort of radio telescope, or rather, half of the telescope.

The unique layout of the Cambridge range furnishes clues to the nature of such apparatus. So far I have described only part of the range. If you turned around and faced the other side, you might have to look twice before you believed your eyes. The eastern half of the range is a mirror image of the western half. It contains duplicate equipment in the same relative positions—another "searchlight" antenna, another array of eighty antennas complete with wire netting and another full set of eighteen curved reflectors arranged in two parallel rows. Every piece of apparatus on the western range has its counterpart to the east.

The Cambridge group does not use single-aerial radio telescopes. It specializes in twin-aerial systems, called interferometers, of which the one I have described is the most powerful. Imagine two aerials separated by two hundred yards, and a radio source located overhead and exactly between them, above a hundred-yard marker. In other words, the source is equally distant from both aerials. Under ideal conditions the radio waves it emits will strike the two aerials at exactly the same instant, and exactly "in phase"—that is, the crests or power peaks of the waves will arrive together, reinforcing each other and providing a double electrical "push." The result is a double-strength signal.

As the source moves, the situation changes. Now it is no longer equally distant from the aerials, and its waves no longer arrive simultaneously. When the source is at a certain position, the waves arrive completely out of phase—as the peak-power crest of one wave reaches the nearer aerial, the trough or low-power point of the other wave reaches the further aerial. When that happens, the waves are said to interfere with each other. They cancel each other, and the instrument registers no signal at all. Now as the source continues to move along its course its position changes so that its signals are alternately reinforced and canceled. The result is a series of double-strength and zero signals.

Each kind of telescope produces characteristic records. The record of a radio source moving by the Big Dish type of telescope usually consists of a single inked hump on a strip of chart paper; the peak occurs when the source passes directly across the center of the aerial. But a source moving across the twin aerials of an interferometer leaves a record of many humps as it passes through successive zero and double-strength positions.

Observations with twin-aerial instruments yield a great deal of information. In a typical record, for example, precise measurements of the time when the highest peak occurs can be used to calculate the position of the radio source along a line parallel to the horizon. The time between the highest peak and the one next to it can be used in calculating the source's angle of elevation in the sky. Analysis of the heights of the humps on the record may indicate whether the radio source is a compact "point" source or an extended formation, relative to the reception cones of the telescope. Another valuable technique is to study the records of a source for different aerial spacings.

The Cambridge searchlight aerials used together as an interferometer led to the discovery of important radio sources. The first eight months of hard work with the telescope produced some of the most precise measurements ever made in radio astronomy. The positions of the most intense or "brightest" radio sources were determined to an accuracy of a sixtieth of a degree of arc or less. This feat reduced by a factor of a hundred the area of sky known to include certain sources. It represents the difference between looking for an object somewhere in the Waldorf-Astoria Hotel and in a summer bungalow.

Among other important studies, the largest Cambridge telescope, the twin array of radio towers, has recently completed a survey of the skies and located many new radio sources. Other discoveries can be expected in the near future.

Twin-aerial instruments are being used at radio observatories in the United States and abroad. Some of them differ radically from the usual twin-aerial systems. One of the first interferometers built stands in Sydney, Australia, on the top of a 250-foot cliff that plunges straight down into the sea. The site was a radar lookout during World War II, and the instrument includes certain design features found in battleship and coastal radar sets. It is unusual in having only one aerial, a dish-shaped affair. It obtains zero and double-strength signals by the canceling effects of two radio waves from the source being observed, one arriving by the direct route and the other bouncing off the sea surface first.

The Australians, the world's most prolific builders of ingenious radio telescopes, have come up with other unique ideas. They have built an interferometer whose aerials are separated by a distance of nearly ten miles (other things being equal, the instrument's resolving power increases as the space between the aerials is widened). But these aerials are not connected by cables, which would be prohibitively awkward and expensive, but by a "radio link." This involves two distinct broadcastings. First the source sends its signals to one aerial, then a man-made transmitter rebroadcasts the signals to the other aerial. Considerable research is being done on radio links and other schemes, as investigators develop greater and greater skill in electronics.

While we are on the subject of Australian radio telescopes, Bernard Mills's unusual and valuable one deserves special mention. Some time ago Mills approached a local farmer with one of the most extraordinary propositions in real-estate history. He wanted to lease some of the farmer's grazing land, a plot in the shape of a cross. The plot now contains a sharp-focus telescope which in a sense combines the features of dish-type and twin-aerial instruments. It consists of two intersecting strips of chicken wire, supported several feet from the ground by what look like fence posts. Each strip is more than a quarter of a mile long, and the entire system has been nicknamed the Southern Cross. The chicken-wire strips are reflectors for radio waves. The "fence posts" are twelve hundred individual antennas which pick up the signals.

There is a similar but somewhat larger instrument, built with Mills's help, on a 96-acre plot at one of the Carnegie Institution's Department of Terrestrial Magnetism stations near Washington, D.C. Other radio telescopes include a long trough-shaped wave trap in Canada, and a striking system of coiled antennas in Ohio.

All these instruments have special uses in the various kinds of research that will be described later on.

## VARIETIES OF INTERFERENCE

Radio astronomers would like nothing better than foolproof instruments, static-free atmospheric conditions and a site remote from most of the activities of civilized society. They would find life a great deal simpler if the only problem were gathering and interpreting astronomical facts. But many things come between observers and the stars. Static produced by electric razors, automobiles, airplanes and a legion of other sources may jam signals coming from interstellar space. Another kind of interference is equally annoying, and sometimes more difficult to control. It has nothing to do with electronics, but it illustrates the variety of troubles which beset investigators.

Radio telescopes are usually built in the country, among farms and open fields. That leaves them vulnerable to hazards which rarely confront scientists accustomed to working inside the laboratory. Trinity College of Cambridge University has an organization known as the Trinity Foot Beagles, a hare-and-hound society for people who have dogs and who like chasing rabbits. Last winter the group decided to hunt hares near the radio-telescope range and sent the Cavendish Laboratory a polite note promising to "keep away from the radio station."

The hunt did not work out according to plan. Four days later the group's leader sent another note: "Sir, I write to apologize for the fact that some of our hounds ran over the ground in your radar station. . . . I am afraid there were such numerous hares that we were unable to stop them. However, I should like to give the assurance that absolutely no damage was done." Despite the assurance, however, an inspection revealed that damage had been done. The hounds of the Trinity Foot Beagles had broken a number of aerial wires strung across the ground. On other occasions frisky Cambridge horses have leaped fences and damaged expensive cables with their hoofs. (Before the war, when the site was being used for other purposes, a horse bit a cable in two and was electrocuted.) Although they do less damage, cows and ducks from neighboring farms are a nuisance too.

People also cause trouble from time to time. Apparently electronic apparatus lying in the open offers an irresistible temptation to occasional visitors. One night someone sneaked into the Cambridge range and ripped a supply of brass pipes from a radio telescope as it was surveying the skies for new radio stars. The disturbance produced a strange "signal" on the records, marking the exact time of the theft, but the culprit was never caught. Scavengers equipped with wire cutters have taken hundreds of dollars' worth of electronic parts from the radio observatory in Sydney. Australian scientists discourage illegal activities with signs reading DANGER—1000

VOLTS, although the aerials carry only a few millionths of a volt.

Fortunately, such difficulties occur only now and then. But disturbances from electrical devices pose a continual problem. Radio and television stations often interfere with broadcasts from space, and the situation has become increasingly complicated during recent years. For example, investigators at the Department of Terrestrial Magnetism sometimes feed interstellar signals into a radio loudspeaker. Two years ago they focused a radio telescope on a powerful radio source. The source came in with a characteristic "whoosh" or rushing sound. But a more familiar sound was competing with the radio star; the aerial had also picked up the music of a symphony being broadcast from a local FM station.

Some interference cannot be located. During one period of more than six months, the Washington radio astronomers learned to recognize the indistinct sounds of a man's voice. The voice was heard regularly, about twice a month and always in the morning. Sometimes it lasted hours, sometimes only a few minutes. Judging by the drone in the background, it was coming from an aircraft, probably a military plane. But the identity of the plane and its mission were never discovered. When this sort of interference is registered on chart paper instead of a loudspeaker, it may produce a mess of jagged lines which mask radio-source records completely. The records of other laboratories have been spoiled by everything from radar sets and taxicab intercom systems to the radio waves emitted by atom-smashing cyclotrons.

Motor ignition systems may also create considerable static, since electricity sputtering across the terminals of spark plugs generates high-frequency radio waves. Ryle's group at Cambridge once had to organize "suppressor squadrons" to silence the static coming from tractors during the harvest season. As soon as the tractors started jamming radio-telescope signals, investigators would hop on bicycles or run over fields and ditches carrying suppressors in their pockets. These bakelite-insulated gadgets, about the size of a cigarette, can be attached to spark plugs to eliminate static. After explaining things to the farmers, the squadrons would install the devices in the tractors and hurry back to work.

A notable interference problem that affected the Big Dish at Jodrell Bank was carried to the floor of Parliament. Housing had to be built for sixty thousand persons, the overflow from crowded Manchester, and the Chamber of Commerce of a nearby town wanted the business. But traffic, toasters, TV sets and other sources would have produced so much static that the 250-foot telescope could not have been operated. Either the Big Dish or the housing project had to go, and at least one member of Parliament got up to say that he thought it should be the instrument. Lovell won that fight. But he won only after weeks of political maneuvering, and after an indignant delegation of businessmen had barged into his office and asked him to go away.

All these kinds of interference are serious problems in radio astronomy. They spoil reception on radio telescopes just as the lights of a city may ruin seeing conditions for optical telescopes. (During wartime blackouts in nearby Los Angeles the Mount Wilson telescope was used more effectively than at any other time.) And with so many interests competing for the use of radio-wave broadcasting bands—radio and television stations, taxicab companies, military and civilian aircraft and so on—sooner or later radio astronomy must have its allotted channels. American investigators might benefit by having a representative on the Federal Communications Commission, as their British colleagues do on the equivalent agency in England.

## SIGNALS AND NOISE

Even under the best observing conditions, exceedingly complex instruments may be required to receive signals from space. Man-made static is not the only serious difficulty. The heavens themselves emit a great flood of interfering static— and they cannot be silenced. Steadily and continuously, from all parts of the sky, there is an intense outpouring of radio waves, an unceasing barrage of radiations reaching the earth. This is known as the galactic background. Whenever radio astronomers "go on the air," and in whatever direction they point their telescopes, galactic background signals come in strongly and on a crude instrument would bury all other records.

This permanent electronic "glow" is many times more powerful than the radiations coming from even the brightest radio sources. Yet out of a chaos of static, radio astronomers manage to detect almost inconceivably faint signals. The way they do it is easy to describe, but not so easy to put into practice. Suppose you wanted to record radio waves coming from a radio source in the Milky Way. You could start by pointing a radio telescope somewhere else, a suitable distance to one side of the source, toward a region of sky where there are no strongly localized radio sources. In other words, you would be observing "pure" galactic background.

Next, swing the telescope around and point it directly at the source. Now you are measuring galactic background signals, plus the signal coming from the radio source. Since the background may not vary greatly for small regions of the sky, all you have to do is subtract it from the total signal, and the remainder represents the source's individual contribution. Radio astronomers use an analogous system, except that they do not actually shift their aerials back and forth. Their equipment is designed to pick up radio sources and background at once in a fixed position and, in effect, to perform all calculations automatically.

The best radio telescopes can detect a radio source whose signal is only about one hundred thousandth as strong as that of the galactic background. This is somewhat like picking out one person's voice in the madly cheering crowd at an Army-Navy football game.

Even after the tiny signals are picked out from the vast outpouring of galactic radio waves, they can be swamped by another kind of static and lost entirely. This static comes from the radio telescope itself. It is the sound of electrons as they zigzag back and forth in vacuum tubes. The negatively charged

*The new radio window is much wider than the one used in conventional astronomy . . .*

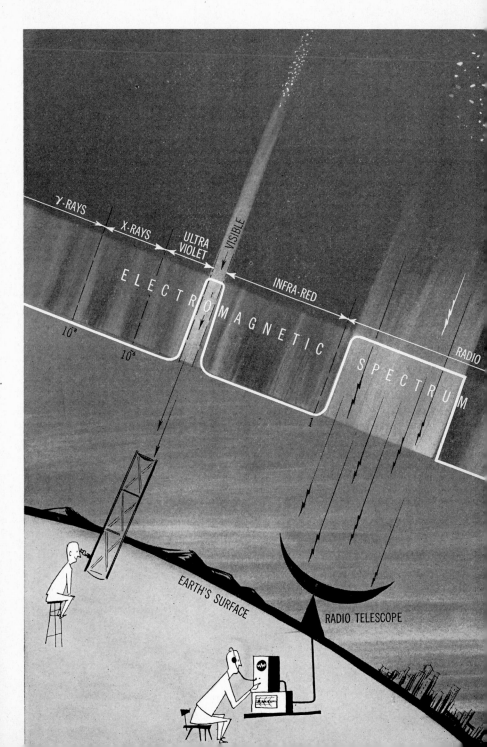

*Radio telescope array at the Radiophysics Laboratory in Sydney, Australia.*

*250-foot Jodrell Bank radio telescope in England.*

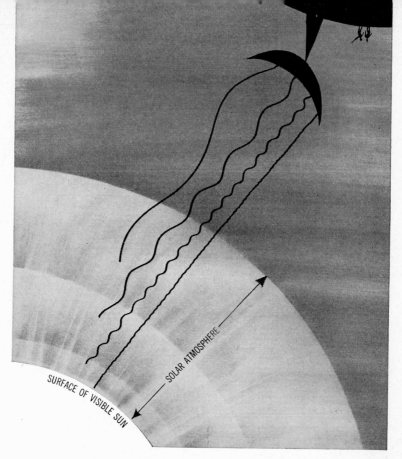

SURFACE OF VISIBLE SUN

SOLAR ATMOSPHERE

*. . . choosing shorter and shorter wave lengths makes it possible to look deeper and deeper into the sun's atmosphere . . .*

*(Below, left) Radio telescope (cylindrical paraboloid) of the Naval Research Laboratory in Washington, D.C.; used for solar studies in Khartoum, Sudan.*

*(Below, right) Radio telescope (interferometer type) at the Radio-physics Laboratory in Sydney, Australia; used in solar studies.*

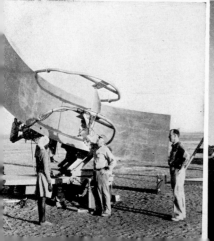

SEXTANT FIXES ON _ _ _ _ _ _ _ AND FOLLOWS SUN

Sun

The radio sextant, a small radio telescope.

atomic particles are never at rest, and their random movements produce electric currents which register on recording equipment and cannot be eliminated. These false signals set a definite limit on the "quietness" of the receiver.

Tune your radio set to a position where there is no station. Now turn up the volume. You hear a very faint crackling or "frying" sound in the background. You are listening to electrons buzzing about in the tubes of your set. They also produce "snow" on television screens. Signals from broadcasting stations easily overpower such static, so that you are unaware of it as you switch on your favorite programs. But things are quite different in the receiver of a radio telescope. The noise in its tubes is a great deal louder than radio-source signals. Moreover, these are the signals that have already been isolated from a galactic background up to a hundred thousand times more powerful—and now we have to distinguish between them and receiver noise.

A characteristic of receiver noise is that it fluctuates widely and suddenly. In this respect it resembles the noise of surf on a beach. In between the sounds of breaking waves come qui-

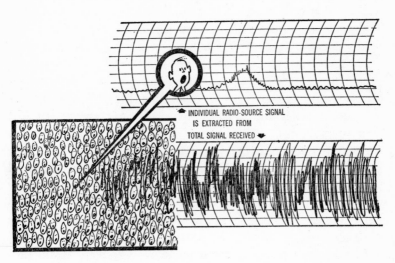

INDIVIDUAL RADIO-SOURCE SIGNAL
IS EXTRACTED FROM
TOTAL SIGNAL RECEIVED

*. . . like picking out one person's voice in a cheering crowd.*

eter intervals, when you hear only ripples and the sweep of
water along sand. Then more breakers, more quiet intervals,
and the occasional crash of really big waves. The noise of electrons in vacuum tubes also comes in unpredictable surges, and
such variations, more than the total noise itself, are what interfere seriously with signals from radio sources.

Once again the radio astronomer calls on his knowledge of
electronics to meet the difficulty. Suppose that at a given instant a radio intensity of 1,100 units is recorded. This is a
mixed message. Part of it is receiver noise; part is the signal
coming from the radio source in space. To find out which is
which, the investigator may build into his radio telescope a
special generator which produces a standard controlled signal of, say, 10 units' intensity.

He arranges things so that at the very same instant the
standard signal is also affected by the receiver noise. This time
the total intensity turns out to be 1,010 units. Clearly the extra 1,000 units represent the effect of noise. So that figure is
subtracted from the original mixed message (1,100 units),
leaving a radio-source signal of 100 units. As usual, the radio
telescope performs all the arithmetic automatically and
swiftly, thirty or more times a second. Such techniques make
it possible to record radio-source signals less than one tenth
of one per cent as strong as the noise in the observing telescope.

Radio telescopes are among the most sensitive instruments
ever designed, and the bodies they detect transmit radio waves
of enormous power. But by the time the radiation travels
trillions of miles and reaches the earth's surface, it has lost
most of its energy. The strongest signals received from outside
the solar system are the broadcasts of a radio source some
10,000 light-years away. The power of these signals, as picked
up by an average-sized aerial, is one hundred billionth of a
watt. It takes about two watts—two hundred billion times
more power—to run an electric clock, and five hundred watts
for a coffee percolator.

Remember, this is a comparison with extremely strong signals. The power of signals from faint radio sources may be
hundreds of times weaker. Another example indicates the sen-
sitiveness of modern aerials. Each human being is an emitter

of radio waves, a living broadcasting station of exceedingly low power. The stomach wall, one of the warmest parts of the body, sends out not only infrared heat waves but the entire spectrum of light, ultraviolet rays, X-rays, radio waves and so on. Of course, all these radiations are fantastically weak and the radio waves are among the weakest. But the fifty-foot aerial of the Naval Research Laboratory in Washington, the most accurately constructed aerial in existence, could pick up radio signals coming from your stomach more than four miles away.

# 4

## LISTENING TO THE SOLAR SYSTEM

On February 27, 1942, British defense outposts received a major scare. That morning, early-warning radar sets at the great harbor city of Southampton detected an intense barrage of static. The static was not coming from local interference or any familiar source. It was widespread, unusually powerful, and long-lasting. Similar effects were being observed at the same time at Yarmouth, Bristol, Hull and a large number of other stations in the nation's elaborate radar network.

Such scares were common during the war. Many of them turned out to be false alarms—radar echoes bouncing off barrage balloons, meteors and even birds. But this was static on a grander scale. The first thought of most observers was the possibility that the Nazis had come up with a secret weapon. Among the most effective anti-radar devices are static producers or "jammers," which fill the air with so much radio noise that it is impossible to detect signals from attacking bombers. Perhaps the disturbances on British radar screens were coming from a great many new Nazi jamming devices. If so, they were probably the prelude to a mass air raid.

One of the investigators called in to help solve the problem was Stanley Hey, whose work on tracking V-2 rockets has already been mentioned. The physicist headed a section of the Army Operational Research Group near London, in the village of Petersham (population 592). The section, which specialized in studies of jamming devices and strange radar echoes, received a mass of reports on the powerful static. The static continued all day on the twenty-seventh and all the next day—and still no Nazi attacks. The immediate scare was over, but the mystery was greater than ever. Hey visited radar sites, talked with operators and examined their records. Then he retired to his office in the attic of Petersham's old vicarage, and waded through all the information.

After a couple of evenings of work, Hey prepared a special memorandum. The report was top secret at the time—only about half a dozen persons read it in full—and some of the details are still classified. The evidence left no room for doubt. Interference was not coming from Nazi radar jammers, but from a more remote and strictly neutral source—the sun. The static appeared at sunrise and faded out at sunset. All radar sets had been pointing in the direction of the sun, and two operators had actually noted the sun's position while the interference was strongest. The disturbances vanished with the passing of a large sunspot.

## NOISY SATELLITES

The discovery marked the first positive identification of radio waves from natural transmitters at the heart of the solar system, 93,000,000 miles away. Since then considerable research has been done on the sun's broadcasts, and most of this and the next chapter will be devoted to such studies. But other members of the solar system have also been seen in radio light. In coming years radio astronomers can be expected to pay more attention to relatively close objects, because recent work has uncovered some interesting problems and one hitherto unobserved type of celestial disturbance.

Weak radio waves are coming from the moon. Some of them, like the light of the moon, consist of second-hand signals. They are emitted by the sun, strike the moon and bounce off toward the earth. Other waves are truly lunar, being produced by transmitters on the moon itself, agitated atoms which send out rays as they move back and forth. Our radio telescopes detect waves that almost entirely represent signals originating in the moon, and the records furnish an excellent example of how such signals from space are interpreted. There is certainly no obvious connection between lunar signals and the nature of the moon's surface. Yet we can use radio techniques to examine the surface, to study the covering of a satellite many thousands of miles away.

As far as light rays from the moon are concerned, we receive most radiation on full-moon nights. On such nights the bright side of the moon, the side toward the sun, faces us completely. But this is not what happens by radio light. The peak intensity of lunar radio waves comes at least three to four days *after* the optical moon has reached its full stage. All the phases of the radio moon lag similarly behind the phases of the visible moon. Such observations have been made by the Australians and the Naval Research Laboratory in Washington, tuning in on lunar radio signals at wave lengths of half an inch and a third of an inch respectively.

To account for the lateness of the phases of the radio moon, investigators have turned to the familiar fact that it takes longer to heat the interior than the outer surface of a body. When the moon is exposed to the heat of the sun, the temperature of the surface naturally rises faster than that of underlying layers, and it is the sun's heat that stirs up lunar atoms and causes them to emit radio waves. In other words, when we tune in on lunar radio waves we are listening to broadcasts coming from beneath the surface.

Detailed analysis of the delayed waves shows that they may be produced at a depth of about a foot or two. Another deduction is that the composition of the moon is not the same throughout that depth. In fact, the waves behave as if the moon were covered with a film of fine dust less than a twentieth of an inch thick and made up of pumice, pulverized volcanic rock. Optical studies also hint at the presence of this film, which may be formed by the accumulated material of tiny meteors falling on the lunar surface during the past two billion years or so. Calculations based on radio observations further indicate that the average surface temperature of the whole disk of the new moon is about two hundred degrees below zero Fahrenheit, and that the deep interior lies at a permanent minus forty degrees.

But the most exciting of all solar-system broadcasts arise from regions beyond the moon. A spectacular discovery was announced in the spring of 1955 by Bernard Burke and Kenneth Franklin, of the Department of Terrestrial Magnetism. One evening they were adjusting their large X-shaped aerial. During a break in the work the physicist of the team, Burke, looked up at the sky. He turned to the astronomer Franklin and asked, "What's that bright star?" The "star" was the planet Jupiter. Judging by subsequent developments, the casual question was almost a prediction of things to come, for the very next evening the investigators picked up the first radio signals ever recorded from the largest planet in our solar system.

An amazing aspect of the discovery is that it had not been made long ago. Jupiter's radio broadcasts are extremely strong when they come in, stronger than many previously found radio sources. They should certainly have been observed before— and they were. An Australian worker, C. A. Shain, had tuned in on the broadcasts five or six years ago, without being able to identify them. Burke and Franklin had received similar signals weeks before their discovery, and blamed sputtering tractors on nearby farms. Jupiter was not on the list of suspects, for a good reason.

Cold bodies are notoriously poor emitters, and Jupiter is unimaginably cold. The moon is cold, too, but it lies only 240,000 miles away. Jupiter is half a billion miles away and the temperature of its atmosphere is probably about two hundred degrees below zero. According to one theory, it is covered by a layer of compressed ice 17,000 miles thick. No one expected that such a remote and frigid body could send radio waves to the earth—not even radio astronomers who deal routinely with the unexpected.

An even greater surprise was in store. Jupiter's signals are not steady hisses like those Jansky detected coming from the center of the Milky Way. They appear and disappear in a peculiar fashion. They are sudden and intense bursts of enormously powerful static. In fact, the bursts may be great lightning flashes produced by the crashing encounters of methane-ammonia clouds high in the skies of Jupiter.

If this static is indeed created by Jovian lightning flashes, nothing on earth can compare with them. The lightning strokes in an ordinary thunderstorm generally last a few thousandths of a second, producing intense static, that is, intense by terrestrial standards. Most of Jupiter's radio bursts last half a second to one second, and their total power is a hundred thousand billion times greater than that of an average lightning stroke on earth.

The source of the disturbances has been identified. Shain, re-examining his old records, noted that the great majority of bursts came at a time when a particular region of the planet was facing the earth. Members of the Jupiter Section of the British Astronomical Association found that the region coincided with a spot, perhaps a vast cloud system, in the Jovian atmosphere. At this stage we do not know what processes give rise to such violent conditions; we have yet to learn what forces churn up its clouds, or whether other planets have similar storms. We do know, however, that Jupiter is cold, but certainly not dead.

## THE NEAREST STAR

The most versatile radio source in the solar system is the sun. Australian, British, French, Canadian and American scientists have been active in investigating our star, but interest is worldwide. Work is going on in India, the Gold Coast, Japan, Sweden, the Belgian Congo and other countries. Altogether, more than fifty radio instruments are being used to observe the sun. A major reason for the widespread interest is one that has been recognized for centuries. The sun is the only star we can study in great detail. Much of what we deduce about more distant suns, the stars of the Milky Way and other galaxies, is based on solar research.

All but one of the stars which we can make out as individual bodies appear as mere pinpoints of light on our most sensitive photographic plates. Located right in our own backyard, the sun is the only star that appears as a disk. It is an accessible sample of the universe of enduring stars, a close-at-hand model whose behavior furnishes important clues to the origin and evolution of solar systems beyond the limits of our observing devices.

The model is an excellent one. The universe is populated with many kinds of stars. Considering size, for example, the volume of one of the biggest—Antares, located near the claws of the Scorpion constellation—is spacious enough to hold 64,000,000 of our suns. And recent studies show that the constellation of Hercules contains a star a hundred million times more voluminous than Antares. On the other hand, the sun itself could hold 125,000 bodies the size of the smallest star, a pygmy that occupies less space than the earth. Stars also differ widely in temperature and brightness and density, and among them the sun rates as an ordinary, run-of-the-mill body.

Of course, what astronomers consider ordinary may be quite spectacular to the rest of us. The sun shines by a self-consuming process. It literally eats its heart out as it burns up the hot gases of its core at temperatures as high as forty million degrees. In the process the nuclei of hydrogen atoms are combined to form helium, a reaction known as nuclear fusion and used on earth as the principle of the hydrogen bomb and other weapons. The amount of energy produced is enormous. As you read the previous sentence, the sun consumed and lost twelve million tons of its gases.

Suppose you picked up your newspaper tomorrow morning and saw the following front-page headline: ASTRONOMERS PREDICT DEATH OF SUN—NO MORE SUNSHINE AFTER 1976—UNITED NATIONS DECLARES INTERNATIONAL EMERGENCY. Suppose also that the twenty-year period of grace was sufficient for us to extract from the earth every ounce of our coal, petroleum and other fuels. How long would they last after the sun sputtered out? If we burned our fuels at the sun's present rate, they would be used up entirely in three days—that is, all but the uranium. Nuclear fuels would be good for another hour or so.

Only a small fraction of the sun's energy—about a thousand billion watts—is released in the form of radio waves, but these broadcasts are transmitting new information, particularly about the solar atmosphere or corona. Astronomers have long been handicapped in their efforts to study the soft, pearly halo surrounding the sun, because its light is only about half as intense as that of the full moon, or one-millionth as intense as the blazing central disk of the sun.

For many years studies of the corona had to be carried out in a hurry, during the brief intervals when the disk was blacked out. Since the development of modern telescopes, the time when the sun has been in total eclipse amounts to only about fifteen minutes, which is hardly enough for leisurely research. Recent advances include special optical instruments which make it possible to study the atmosphere of the sun without waiting for eclipses, but these instruments are most useful in scanning parts of the corona relatively close to the central disk. Outer portions emit too little light.

Exactly the opposite situation exists when the sun is observed with radio telescopes. The disk, which shines so brightly in the optical part of the spectrum, is not an intense radio transmitter. Furthermore, a large percentage of the radio waves it does produce are scattered by the corona and never reach us. The corona itself, on the other hand, emits radio waves far more powerfully than the disk. While the optical sun consists of a bright core with an invisible atmosphere, the radio sun is a dark core with a very bright halo. The radio sun is much bigger than the optical sun because the corona extends far beyond the visible edges of the sun and transmits radiations which produce signals in our receiving aerials.

How far does the corona extend? Radio astronomy provides several ways of answering this question, and one of the most interesting has been used on the Rifle Range at Cambridge University. The method depends on a type of radio eclipse.

A source of intense radio waves is located in the constellation Taurus, the Bull. Like other radio sources, it can be observed during the day as well as at night. Every June the Taurus source is eclipsed by the sun—that is, by the radio sun, for the visible disk of the sun does not come directly between the nebula and the earth. In fact, the edge of the disk is nearly two million miles to one side of the source at its closest approach. The eclipse is produced by the corona, which first reduces, and later cuts off entirely, radio signals from the Taurus source. The effect can be compared to what happens when a cloud moves across a star and hides its light, but in this case the "cloud" is the sun's atmosphere and the "star" is a radio source.

In June, 1954, two Cambridge investigators, Kenneth Machin and Graham Smith, set up their radio telescope and awaited developments. The total eclipse lasted two days. On June 14 and 15 Taurus signals disappeared, blocked off entirely by the solar corona. But even more significant, the signals started growing weaker as early as June 9 and did not return to their normal level until about ten days later. The outer regions of the sun's atmosphere were moving across the Taurus source long before the regions nearer the visible solar disk reached it.

Machin and Smith arrived at a figure for the extent of the corona by precise measurements of the relative positions of sun and source, and the duration of the eclipse. Their findings indicate that the distance from the center of the sun to the outer edge of the corona is at least twenty times the radius of the visible sun. That represents an over-all radius of 8,640,000 miles. It is this giant disk which we would observe rising in the east and setting in the west if our eyes were sensitive enough to see the main part of the corona. The area of this sun would appear several hundred times greater than that of the familiar sun.

Such new observations greatly extend the evidence accumulated by conventional astronomy during the past century. They reveal the sun as a ball of flaming gases surrounded by a corona so thin that we cannot see it without sensitive instruments. Moreover, the sun's atmosphere, like the earth's, becomes thinner as it goes higher. Millions of miles above the surface of the sun, the gases are still sufficiently dense to cut off some of the radio waves traveling from the Taurus source.

But the radio evidence does not mean the corona ends at that height. It simply means we are approaching the limits of our present-day radio telescopes. More sensitive instruments would locate an outer edge at a greater distance from the center of the sun. Presumably the "real" edge would prove as elusive as the end of the rainbow, for the corona extends far into space and fades away by imperceptible degrees. Strictly speaking, it has no definite dimensions. So if we could see the radio sun it would not be a sharply defined disk. It would have no edges and would merge gradually with the radio sky.

The tenuous fringes of the corona may actually extend as far as the earth's orbit. A faint, ghostly glow can sometimes be seen in clear moonless skies. In northern latitudes it comes at nightfall in the spring and before dawn in autumn; in the tropics it is visible all year round. It may have been this glow which appeared to the sailors of *Moby Dick* as the apparitions of the White Whale. According to some investigators, the so-called zodiacal light may arise under special conditions in the furthest reaches of the corona.

If they are correct, traces of the sun's vast atmosphere lie within twenty thousand miles or so of the surface of the earth —the estimated height of the zodiacal light—so its outermost limits are relatively close at hand. However, radio astronomers so far have observed only the main body of the corona, which extends some nine to twelve million miles beyond the rim of the visible sun.

## INSIDE THE SUN'S ATMOSPHERE

In January, 1952, John Hagen, Fred Haddock and nine other members of the Naval Research Laboratory landed on a Khartoum airstrip in Africa's Sudan, about four hundred miles from the Red Sea. First they unpacked in their rooms at the Grand Hotel on the left bank of the blue Nile. Then they started installing seventy tons of equipment in the desert. About a hundred and forty astronomers from a dozen nations were staying in Khartoum, most of them at the same hotel, forming what has been described as "perhaps the greatest assembly of eclipse talent that ever existed."

A total eclipse of the sun was expected on February 25. On that day, at 11:12 A.M. sharp, the moon would blot out the sun for three minutes and nine seconds. Sudanese natives place little faith in scientific predictions; they were skeptical but tolerant. They helped set up equipment and watched investigators make adjustments for an event which in their opinion would never come off.

At 9:45 in the morning, "first contact" was made. The moon started crossing the face of the sun. The Naval Research Laboratory report describes what happened: "As the first phase of the eclipse progressed the daylight became dimmer, the breeze became less, and nature seemed to envelop herself in an expectant hush presaging the surprising glory of totality. At 11:12 the face of the sun was blotted out and the corona flashed into view. Mercury and a number of brighter stars appeared. A red hydrogen prominence was visible at the right-hand side of the sun. . . . After totality those groups whose experiments were completed could relax. The two radio-wave groups continued their measurements through the final phase until the end of the eclipse at 12:38 P.M."

Naval radio astronomers were there for several reasons. Although solar radio waves can be studied at any time, with or without the benefit of eclipses, Hagen and his colleagues had planned special experiments. For one thing, they wanted to study the distribution of radio-wave intensities across the radio sun. (The eclipsing moon served as a kind of slow-motion camera shutter, canceling radiations bit by bit as it passed over the face of the sun.) But they also obtained new information for their continuing research on the deepest interior of the sun's atmosphere.

Radio astronomy can do a great deal more than measure the extent of the corona's upper regions. It furnishes new instruments which make up, at least in part, for the fact that our eyes are insensitive to radio waves. It permits us to explore in greater detail the vast globe whose tiny core is the sun we see, to probe far into the corona and even beneath that. Using radio telescopes, we can take radio soundings of this invisible sea of gases. Within certain limits we can tune in to different depths almost as if we were selecting stations on a radio or a television set. This is one reason why workers at the Naval Research Laboratory came to Khartoum.

One known depth, for example, is far inside the sun's atmosphere, only a few thousand miles above its surface. The region is a reasonable facsimile of hell. It is a hot scarlet place known as the chromosphere, the color coming from the characteristic glow of its hydrogen gases. The chromosphere forms a spherical zone or shell about six thousand miles thick between the sun and the corona. All sorts of radio waves are generated by the fast atomic particles whizzing around in this zone—the entire radio spectrum of waves from about a third of an inch to many yards long.

When radio astronomers tune in to different depths of the sun's atmosphere, they are taking advantage of basic properties of radiating matter. Radio waves may result from near-collisions of atomic particles. At the high temperatures of the chromosphere, hydrogen is broken into its electrified parts, positively charged protons and negatively charged electrons. The fragments shoot off in all directions. When an electron comes close to a proton, its path is bent sharply as it passes. Exactly the same thing would happen if a steel bullet just missed a sufficiently powerful magnet. A not-so-close encounter changes the path of the passing electron by a slighter amount, so that its new path is not so sharply curved. The paths of particles that move by at greater distances may hardly be bent at all.

But any appreciable swerving of sufficiently fast electrons under such conditions creates radio waves. The change in direction produces a rapid acceleration, and the excess energy is released in the form of radiations. Moreover, the greater the curvature of the bent path—or the closer the electron comes to colliding with and attracting a proton—the shorter the length of the emitted waves. In other words, near-misses result in sharp bends of electron paths and short radio waves. Long waves are generated when the electrons miss by relatively great distances and swerve only slightly.

The traffic of atomic particles on the go is heavy in the chromosphere. Within a space no larger than a thimble, billions upon billions of near-collisions take place every second. A rich assortment of radio waves is produced, but not all of them get through. In fact, a large proportion never reach the upper regions of the corona, because all this is going on near the solar surface, beneath a towering blanket of gases.

The long waves are nipped in the bud. Unable to penetrate the sun's atmosphere, they bounce back toward their place of origin.

Some radiations do escape, however. Many short radio waves slip out through the corona, travel 93,000,000 miles across space, pour into the earth's atmosphere and strike the aerials of our radio telescopes. These waves are signals straight from the chromosphere and the bottom of the corona. When we tune in on them we are, in effect, looking directly into the depths of the sun's atmosphere, the very regions which have proved most difficult to study by the methods of conventional astronomy. So we select the shortest detectable radio waves to observe the interior.

Suppose we want to explore the upper regions of the corona, extending hundreds of thousands of miles above the roof of the chromosphere. In that case, we tune in on long radio waves. The gases of the upper regions are less dense than those lower down; the traffic of atomic particles is considerably lighter. Very close encounters between protons and electrons —the near-misses which produce short radio waves—are tremendously reduced. Not-so-close encounters are far more frequent among thinner upper gases; the result is a heavy predominance of long radio waves.

Radio telescopes designed to receive these long waves observe events taking place high in the corona. A telescope tuned to a wave length of about fifteen yards, for example, would be detecting signals generated some 300,000 miles up in the corona. Choosing shorter and shorter wave lengths makes it possible to look deeper and deeper into the sun's atmosphere, step by step. It is something like peeling off the successive layers of an onion. An instrument tuned to five-yard waves "sees" things happening at a depth of about 125,000 miles. At a rough estimate, the 25,000-mile layer can be observed at a four-foot wave length, the 6,000-mile layer at a twenty-five-inch wave length, and so on. . . .

In the Sudan, the Naval Research investigators were interested in the deepest regions of the chromosphere. They chose to listen in at a wave length of about a third of an inch. The reflector of their radio telescope, a so-called cylindrical parabola, was a strange sight on the Sudan desert. It consisted of a shining arc of sheet metal sixteen feet long and resembling a curved portion of a children's slide. Interesting results were obtained from research in Khartoum as well as from previous and more recent work in Alaska, Washington and Sweden.

These studies indicate that the chromosphere is not uniform throughout its entire volume. If a recent theory is correct, it may contain small regions or "cells" in which conditions vary enormously. Temperatures as high as eighty thousand degrees Fahrenheit may prevail in one cell, while a neighboring cell may be cold by comparison. Just above the chromosphere, extending from its 6,000-mile roof to a height of about 15,500 miles into the base of the corona, is a shell of gases in which the temperature rises rapidly to nearly two million degrees.

These findings are only some of the earliest yielded by radio-sun studies. Other findings will be described in the next chapter; still others are yet to come.

The African expedition is already ancient history in the rapidly growing field of radio astronomy, but it represents an important event in the exploration of the radio sun. After completing their work, a group of radio astronomers in an American Navy truck rolled out of Khartoum and through the city's outskirts. The road was lined with cheering Sudanese citizens, most of whom had not believed that the sun would black out. "The cheers affected us strangely," an expedition member recalls. "In a way we felt that the eclipse had somehow justified us—and science—in the eyes of the natives."

## RADIO NAVIGATION

Another experiment illustrates one of the most important applications of radio astronomy. More than a year ago, a Navy patrol boat started on a trip from Cuba to New London, Connecticut. At the stern was a searchlight mounting with a bowl-shaped aerial about the size of an umbrella where the searchlight should have been. When the boat was under way, an operator threw a switch. The aerial began rotating and sweeping up and down, surveying the skies like a radar set on the lookout for enemy planes. Then the robot scanner found what it was looking for. It stopped hunting and "locked on" its target. Its electronic eye remained fixed on a moving object.

The object was a star, the sun—but not the visible sun. The day was dark and stormy; gray clouds covered the skies. But the bad weather had no effect on the instrument, a radio telescope specially designed to find and follow the radio sun. Bad weather prevailed most of the way to New London, but every day the telescope furnished accurate information about the sun's position and the position of the ship. The skipper later commented that he would have given his right arm to have had a similar device on his ship during wartime operations in Japanese waters.

This pioneer test marks a new era in celestial navigation. For thousands of years men have been finding their positions at sea by observing the light of the sun and the stars. Our modern knowledge is embodied in the marine sextant, a sighting instrument, and its auxiliary charts and tables. Now for the first time we are beginning to sail by bodies in the radio skies, to find our way with instruments that detect invisible radiations from space. Radio telescopes intended for such purposes are called radio sextants. They are being developed by investigators at the Naval Research Laboratory and the Collins Radio Company in Cedar Rapids, Iowa.

If you stepped near the radio sextant on the patrol boat, you would see a metal rod sticking out from the center of the aerial. The rod is known as the "primary feed," the element through which collected radio waves pass into the receiver. You might notice that there are shiny screws at the tip of the rod, and obtain a kind of flickering impression as you watch them closely. This is the only sign that the tip of the rod is moving rapidly. It is circling at a rate of about thirty revolutions a second, so that it scans continuously around the center of the radio sun like a finger tracing the circumference of a circle.

The rod is sighting the sun. When the sun moves, it begins to pass out of the field of the rotating tip. The instrument senses the motion and turns automatically to keep itself accurately on the target. Exactly the same thing happens when a hunter keeps his sights trained on a running animal. The radio sun is never allowed to "escape." Its image is kept imprisoned within the field of the circling tip—and its position is continuously registered on meters below decks. The sensitive instrument receives short-wave signals (wave length, somewhat less than an inch) which come in at a power level of only about a trillionth of a watt.

The Collins Radio Company has been actively interested in radio sextants for more than a decade. Its observing station is located on Feather Ridge, near the Cedar River. The station is run by David McCoy, assistant director of research and development at Collins, and it lies in the heart of corn-raising country. In fact, the land is so valuable for corn-raising that about twenty local farmers refused to lease any part of their holdings for experiments in such an abstruse subject as radio astronomy.

"Finally, one elderly farmer who isn't doing much work leased us ten acres of his land," McCoy told me. "We fenced off one acre with electrified fences to keep away the cattle that graze after the crops are harvested." The farmer can use the other nine acres, but, "We have an agreement that no corn more than thirty inches tall shall be grown inside the area. If the corn grew any higher than that, it would interfere with low-traveling radio waves coming from the horizon."

McCoy and his associates at Feather Ridge are conducting a full-scale research program in radio astronomy, the only such program in American industry. Their original radio sextant has passed further tests in the Arctic Circle, aboard an icebreaker assigned to the Naval Electronics Laboratory in San Diego. They have also designed a smaller and more compact radio sextant which detects shorter waves and is being tested by the Air Force in a series of secret studies. All that can be said at this time is that the instrument has been built for larger transoceanic aircraft.

Perhaps the chief limitation of these radio sextants is that they are of no use at night, when the sun has set. Ideally, there should be a device that automatically switches from the sun to some other radio object after sunset. One of the objects currently under study for this use is the moon. Lunar radio waves are about twenty to thirty times weaker than those coming from the sun, but indications are that even such feeble signals can serve as guides to steer by, and a sun-moon radio sextant is a definite possibility. In any case, during the next few years we shall be hearing a great deal more about significant advances in radio navigation, a direct outgrowth of new studies of the radio sun.

# 5

## THE SUN IN ACTION

"[The sun's] surface is a seething, surging sea of atoms. Plumes of gas float above it; glowing filaments surge upward; shining fountains cascade downward. Giant tornadoes swirl through the surface. Spicules rise and dissipate like darting flames. Dazzling flares blaze up and vanish. A brilliant chromosphere rings it, and around it gleams the aura of the corona. . . . The spectacle is impressive in itself. As the mirror of the universe, it is stupendous. Other stars are doing the same things. . . ."—from *Stars in the Making* (Harvard University Press).

A leading American investigator, Cecelia Payne-Gaposchkin, of the Harvard College Observatory, uses these vivid words to give us an idea of how the sun appears to astronomers. But the odds are that you will have to take her word for it. The sun as we see it from day to day is not a particularly exciting object. Most of us have never witnessed the startling scenery of the solar inferno, and we can only imagine the full reasons for the astronomer's enthusiasm.

But there are excellent motion pictures of the sun. They show all the varied effects mentioned in the above description, and a great many more, in brilliant detail. They were made at Harvard's stations in Climax, Colorado, and Sunspot, New Mexico, and are among the most exciting films I have ever seen. Unfortunately, they are shown mainly at scientific conventions and other special meetings. You will certainly not get a chance to see them at your neighborhood theatre. The people who distribute motion pictures, like the people who make them, have a limited notion of what interests the rest of us and show no sign of reforming.

If it is any consolation, no one has ever seen what are probably by far the most sensational fireworks in the solar system. None of us, neither astronomers nor laymen, can view the continuous performances of the radio sun. These performances take place on an even vaster stage than those recorded on film, since the area of the radio sun is so much bigger than the visible sun. If you could see the sun as it would appear to eyes capable of detecting radio "light," you might pay more attention to it. You would definitely not ignore it on your way to and from work, no matter how busy you were.

The visible sun is surprisingly steady, considering all the disturbances that are taking place in its interior and on its surface. The brightness of sunlight hardly varies more than a per cent or two over the years. But radio-sun-light would vary spectacularly, because the radio sun is a thing of flickering, pulsating radiations. During the day it may flare up frequently, its intensity increasing ten to many hundred times in violent, unexpected radio fits. On rarer occasions it has been known to grow hundreds of thousands of times brighter within a few seconds. The "light" would then be inconceivably dazzling. People who could see radio waves would have to go around wearing special radio spectacles. Radio-sun-glasses would be fitted with wire-mesh lenses to cut down on radio glare the way our dark lenses cut down on optical glare.

This is the radio sun, the object which astronomers are investigating for the first time. We are learning new facts not only about its structure, but also about the production of powerful radio waves in space. The findings are of considerable importance, practically as well as theoretically.

## A SIMMERING FURNACE

Some years ago Grote Reber arranged a demonstration in the backyard of his home in Illinois. The pioneer radio astronomer had important visitors and he decided to tune in on the sun. It was a cold, rainy November day. Viewing conditions were hopeless for conventional telescopes, but entirely suitable for Reber's pie-plate aerial. Pointing the aerial in the direction of the sun, which was obscured by gray clouds, he switched on his receiving set. The sun was performing in fine style. Out of the loudspeaker came a mad chorus of assorted wheezes, howls, puffs and swishes—the strongest and most varied solar broadcasts he had ever picked up.

Then Reber shifted his aerial to the side, so that it no longer focused on the sun. The symphony of static faded to a steady hiss. Then back to the sun, and the noise came in again. That completed the main part of the demonstration. The visitors, representatives of the National Bureau of Standards, had traveled all the way from Washington to find out how well a sensitive radio telescope would work in actual sky-scanning operations. They went back satisfied, and shortly afterward Reber obtained his position on the Bureau's technical staff.

Reber had assembled a first-rate electronic device. As he swung the aerial away from the sun and back to it, the noise on the loudspeaker faded and then came in strongly and sharply. Instrument noise, a frequent source of static, caused no trouble on this occasion. Of course, the sounds that came in over the loudspeaker were neither the only nor the most important records. Permanent records were obtained in the form of inked lines on moving chart paper. Although humps, peaks and jagged scrawlings do not look very impressive, they reveal a great deal about powerful celestial transmitters.

We find no peace and quiet in the universe, any more than we do on earth. Even at night, in the remotest countryside, something is always stirring, perhaps slow winds moving through trees or around the walls and roofs of farmhouses. We find the same thing when we direct a radio telescope toward space. Something is stirring even when the telescope is focused on a portion of the sky containing no detectable radio stars. The automatic pen of its recorder makes a rippling, tremor-like line on the moving paper. This is the signature of the galactic background, the radio waves that come from unidentified sources in all parts of the Milky Way and beyond. This is the written record of the hissing Karl Jansky heard when he first received signals from space.

The galactic background is always represented by a wavy line located distinctly above the zero-signal level, the record that would be traced if the instrument were receiving no signals. If the telescope is turned toward the sun, the pen rises sharply and may continue writing a similar rippling line at a higher level. The recorder now registers a signal composed of two parts, the galactic background plus the radio output of the sun.

The general appearance of the sun's signals over an appreciable period of time depends on the sort of radio waves being received. Steady records, the rippling-line type, may be obtained at any wave length. They represent the minimum, basic radio intensity of the sun, the output of what radio astronomers call the "quiet sun." At the longest wave lengths, which come from high in the corona, quiet-sun records may be interrupted by spells of extra-intense activity, when the ripples are transformed into huge jagged peaks indicating special solar activity.

We find an entirely different picture at the other end of the radio spectrum. Very short waves, measuring only half an inch or less from crest to crest, originate in the depths of the chromosphere near the solar surface. Radio telescopes designed to pick up these waves register the familiar little ripples almost continuously. The record shows no large deviations in the steady path of the automatic pen. In other words, conditions in the lower regions of the sun's atmosphere are calm and serene most of the time.

Just how quiet is the quiet sun in these regions? Astronomers who use conventional telescopes can tell us what is happening—that is, what is happening visually. Photographs of the sun's surface show that it is curiously mottled. It has a grainy structure, and a rough analogy may help indicate the nature of the individual "granulations." If you look into a pot of boiling water, you see that things are highly agitated at the surface. Bubbles come zigzagging toward the surface, bump into other bubbles, merge and burst as fresh bubbles rise from below.

Similar disturbances are breaking out at the surface of the sun. Each granulation is believed to be a bubble of gases, seething at temperatures of thousands of degrees. The boiling process takes place on an inconceivably vast scale. A solar bubble may be eight hundred miles across, or about the distance from New York to Chicago. It is short-lived, lasting only three minutes or so. At any one time, the surface is covered with more than a million such bubbles, all of which are rising at speeds of about 3,600 miles an hour. Martin Schwarzschild, of Princeton, a leading astronomer in solar and stellar studies, has compared them to whitecaps on a choppy sea.

Photographs of the chromosphere, above the bursting solar bubbles, reveal a kind of delicate ray structure around the entire circumference. The rays stick out like blades of grass or the quills of a porcupine. They are tongues of gas darting up from the surface and probably represent an effect of the huge bubbles underneath. When the bubbles burst, they may emit fountain-jets of gas which flash into the atmosphere and create explosive shock waves. The shock waves resemble those generated by high-speed aircraft which crash through the air and the supersonic barrier. But the shock waves in the sun's atmosphere are enormously more powerful.

On the sun, the bubbles and jets and shock waves are as common as traffic noises in New York City. They are surface phenomena, the outer signs of massive disturbances and explosions originating deep inside the sun. We do not know what causes them. But they may be transmitters and play an important part in producing the short radio waves which register as small ripples on the recorders of radio telescopes—the same waves, by the way, which are detected by radio sextants and used in research on radio navigation. Radio astronomy is expected to help answer many questions about this kind of mild chaos found on the quiet sun.

## CLOUDS IN THE CORONA

The sun is capable of far more violent activity that produces far more intense radiations, but we do not pick these up at the short wave lengths which come from down in the heart of the chromosphere. We would be severely handicapped if we had nothing but short-wave receivers to tune in on the sun. It would be like trying to measure the forces of a roaring Pacific typhoon on the basis of records taken hundreds of fathoms beneath the surface. The depths are relatively quiet. Great undersea currents coil their way sluggishly through the coldest, darkest parts of the ocean—and tell us very little about the turbulence above. The full fury of the storm exists much higher up, in regions where twisting winds are at large.

The same situation holds for many disturbances and massive gas typhoons of the sun. Radio telescopes "see" them most vividly at longer wave lengths emitted high in the corona. Such events differ considerably from the gentle ripples typical of the quiet sun, and leave their jagged markings on the moving charts. Our picture of the radio sun—and in the last analysis, of the entire radio universe—depends on how well we interpret these markings. And interpreting is rarely an easy process. Radio astronomers study their instrument readings as carefully as psychiatrists study brain-wave charts, which, as a matter of fact, sometimes bear a striking resemblance to readings of cosmic static. In both cases the problem is to examine inked records for clues to the nature of extremely complex physical processes.

Interesting effects can be traced to disturbances as much as ten to fifteen thousand miles above the sun's surface. They are observed at radiations in the wave-length range from just under two inches to two feet (waves from the lowest chromosphere are half an inch or less long). The record may show a series of slow "rollers" as radio signals periodically rise and fall in intensity, producing a chart that may remind you of a business-cycle graph with its series of peaks and depressions. But a business cycle may last for years, while the time between successive ups and downs on such solar records may be only a matter of days.

In fact, the radio signals tend to reach their peak intensities every twenty-seven days. This is the length of the solar day, the time it takes the sun to make one complete rotation on its axis. As the sun spins, powerful broadcasting centers spin along with it. The centers sweep the skies like the beacon of a lighthouse, and they show bright and glaring (in radio "light," of course) each time they come around. Then the intensity fades as they swing away with the rotating sun, and rises again as they come around once more.

Intense sources have been studied with many beautifully designed instruments. For example, one of the Australians' most interesting radio telescopes is the so-called 64-element interferometer. Designed by W. N. Christiansen and J. A. Warburton, it lies on a hill near Sydney and is shaped like a capital L. Each arm of the L is nearly three city blocks long, consisting of thirty-two individual searchlight-shaped aerials strung out along the concrete sides of a reservoir. This is a high-resolution, sharp-focus instrument which makes it possible to tune in on radio waves coming from definite and localized solar regions. Using such telescopes, radio astronomers have learned a good deal about signals that rise and fall in twenty-seven-day cycles.

The signals come from agitated radio clouds, expanses of gases whose atoms are moving and colliding at great speeds. A cloud of average size is probably seething away at temperatures of ten million degrees or more. Its area is equivalent to about four-thousandths of the sun's disk, some ten billion square miles or about fifty times the total area of the earth. Most broadcasting clouds in the corona are directly above, or just to one side of, sunspots—great turbulent, splashing depressions or "holes" in the surface of the sun. In general, the clouds disappear when the sunspots disappear. It seems that sunspot disturbances at the surface stir up parts of the corona into producing strong radio waves. Sometimes the disturbances linger in a kind of electronic afterglow. They keep on emitting even after the sunspots originally associated with them have vanished completely.

## NOISE STORMS

For more dramatic solar programs, radio astronomers can tune in to still longer radiations. In the wave-length range from about one to fifteen yards these extra-strong broadcasts come in clearly, with plenty of volume, but quite unpredictably. As at shorter wave lengths, the record is steady, or fairly steady, most of the time. Then all at once the record may change radically. The automatic pen which has been writing along on a relatively even keel for some time may suddenly start climbing to a new level and register continuous high-intensity signals. Actual records show that the signals come in with up to a thousand times more power than those of the quiet sun. The long-wave radio sun becomes a thousand times "brighter."

Such disturbances, called noise storms, may last hours or days. They take place mainly in the higher portions of the corona, although their roots sometimes extend deep. Their effects have been observed on twenty-inch-wave records coming from lower regions, many thousands of miles nearer the sun's surface. While an aerial is tuned to a noise storm, the recording pen generally works overtime. It may be deflected violently and repeatedly, as if it were held in an invisible hand that had suddenly gone out of control. The resulting "spikes" are telltale signs of sharp, fast blasts of static, heard as crashing sounds if you listen in with earphones. According to one investigator, such signals "must be caused by something similar to lightning flashes, but more terrific."

Noise storms are usually associated with disturbances above sunspots. In this respect they resemble the signals which rise and fall in twenty-seven-day cycles, but they come through on longer wave lengths, take place higher in the corona and are caused by extremely large sunspots. The first storm traced definitely to such a sunspot, in the face of skepticism on the part of certain prominent scientists, was the one studied by Stanley Hey back in 1942, and temporarily mistaken for a new Nazi anti-radar measure. Since then many radio sunspot storms have been observed and a great many more can be expected during the next five years or so. Sunspots tend to come in cycles of about eleven years, and we are entering a period of increased sunspot activity. The peak of the current cycle should occur around 1958 or 1959.

Trained investigators manage to extract an amazing number of facts from radio-telescope charts. They find, interwoven in what seems like a meaningless jumble of jagged lines and humps, markings that represent the most valuable thing in science—information. In the scrawlings of automatic pens they see clues to the characteristics of storms raging at remote places in space. They compare the spikes and other markings on their charts with events seen through conventional telescopes, and try to match the two. For one important example, they have noticed that as a rule noise-storm broadcasts coincide with the passing of huge spots across the face of the sun. Intensive analysis of very fine detail continues to reveal more and more information—increasingly subtle facts—about these storms in different sorts of records. Radio waves streaming from the distant storms are recognizable by a peculiar and significant property that is charted with special interferometer-type radio telescopes.

Storm radiations can be recorded on regular charts, but much better information is provided by another widely used kind of recorder. This instrument is known as a cathode-ray oscilloscope, or simply CRO. It has no automatic pen. Its writing is done by a moving "finger" or beam of electrons which draws bright green lines on the fluorescent surface of a television-type screen. When an interferometer telescope with its aerials set at right angles is picking up waves from out in the galaxy, or from the quiet sun, the CRO screen shows straight horizontal lines only. Under the same receiving conditions blasts of radiation from solar storms produce distinctive records, curves consisting of one or two peaks with a dip between, a kind of hill-and-valley pattern.

Such records indicate that the radiation comes from an unusual kind of region. Most radio waves from space are produced by atoms moving randomly and chaotically in all directions, like bees in a stirred-up hive or water bugs on the surface of a pond. But a different kind of wave results when the atoms are "regimented" in some way, when some force sets large numbers of them moving together with a co-ordinated rhythm like the dancing Rockettes. This is the radiation which makes peaked curves on the recording screens of right-angle aerial systems. It is known as "polarized" radiation.

The forces that polarize solar radio waves, and that tend to order the chaotic movements of atomic particles, are enormously powerful magnetic fields associated with sunspots. At one time a sunspot was thought to be a spinning vortex resembling a whirlpool or the swirl of water down a drain. This theory is no longer tenable (although it continues to linger well past its time in the pages of many recent astronomical textbooks). It could take a thousand years to create or destroy such a vortex, and sunspots appear and disappear in a matter of weeks.

We know that a sunspot is a depression in the sun's surface which may be as much as a hundred thousand miles across. The entire earth could plummet into an abyss that large and vanish without producing a ripple—a drop in the solar bucket. There is a good deal of splashing in and around the hole. Streamers, ribbons and sprays of hot gases shoot out like incandescent confetti, climbing and twisting to heights of half a million miles or more above the surface of the sun. According to recent theories, sunspots are places where great rings of magnetic force inside the sun snap out like steel springs released through the surface. Or they may be the results of supersonic shock waves speeding from the center of the sun. But the basic causes of sunspots are not yet known. The co-existence of many different theories is a sign that much remains to be learned.

Whatever is going on, atomic particles are whipped into spiraling, rapid motion. Intense magnetic fields are present and radio waves passing through them are polarized so that they oscillate in a unique way and leave characteristic records. From the records radio astronomers can tell whether the magnetic fields of sunspots have their north or south poles pointing toward the earth. There may also be clues to sudden changes in the poles. A giant spot usually moves at the head of a group of spots, leading the parade. But sometimes it may shift and suddenly trail the group. This action produces a switch of magnetic poles and a change on the recorder of the observing radio telescope. The intense, curving green line of the telescope's screen also shifts by a fraction of an inch. By such delicate signs we explore radio storms raging 93,000,000 miles from earth.

## BURSTS OF POWER

Storms may continue for several days. They can be definitely classed among the sun's more sustained performances, full-length programs from solar radio stations. But there are also "spot broadcasts," brief interludes of intense radiation called outbursts. The disturbances may be picked up at any wave length, which means they may be produced at any level of the chromosphere and corona.

The most powerful radio outburst on record was observed on March 8, 1947, in Australia. Investigators at Sydney and on Mount Stromlo listened in with three radio telescopes tuned to three different wave lengths, all three tracking the sun at once. First indications of the event were noted at exactly 4:25½ A.M., when the instrument tuned to the shortest wave length, about five feet, registered a sharp increase in radio intensity. Then two minutes passed before another unusually large increase was detected on the receiver tuned to longer waves (ten-footers). Again a delay, this one lasting four minutes, and finally another big signal—this time on the recorder of the telescope receiving the longest, fifteen-foot waves. During this period the brightness of the radio sun increased more than a million times.

The Australians lost no time in analyzing these results. The first signals, the five-foot waves, originate about 20,000 miles above the solar surface. The ten-foot waves that were detected after the two-minute delay usually arise at a level some 60,000 miles higher in the corona. The final barrage of fifteen-foot waves was known to come from regions about 70,000 miles higher still.

Could the entire sequence of signals be emitted by the same source, a single source shooting up through the corona at a speed of 17,500 to 30,000 miles a minute? This was the Australians' original interpretation. Paul Wild and his associates have confirmed it in many subsequent studies, using a radio telescope which consists of three aerials. These aerials, which with their long extensions resemble a new kind of electronic gun, make it possible to follow rising solar outbursts at wave lengths of from about four to twenty-five feet—that is, from heights of 20,000 to more than 200,000 miles above the sun's surface. Astronomers at a new Harvard station in Fort Davis, Texas, are working on a similar instrument.

Optical astronomers working closely with radio astronomers have identified the cause of the outbursts. For example, for nearly two years Charles Seeger and other radio astronomers listened in to solar broadcasts at Cornell University. During the same period, Helen Dodson and her associates at the Mc-Math-Hulbert Observatory photographed disturbances from a fifty-foot solar tower. A detailed comparison of the records showed that radio outbursts followed four out of every five solar "flares"—sudden blazes of intense light, usually eruptions of sizzling hydrogen gas near sunspots. In a few cases observers actually timed outbursts with streams of matter, hydrogen and calcium, being ejected from the sun at the beginning of a flare. Incidentally, the great outburst of March, 1947, occurred during a flare.

Why did only four out of five, not five out of five, flares seem to produce outbursts. The reason may be that in these studies radio observations were made at five-foot wave lengths, or about twenty thousand miles above the sun's surface. "At that height we're probably seeing secondary effects only," an investigator explained. "When we tune in on ten-centimeter [four-inch] waves, we're right on top of things, down near where flares occur. Then practically every single flare produces a detectable radio outburst."

Other more mysterious radio disturbances occur only at longer wave lengths, in the outer layers of the corona. Storms may last for days, outbursts for minutes, but these extra-fast flashes of radio power appear and disappear within a few seconds. They, too, have been observed as they dash up through the corona, and their speeds are enormous—up to sixty thousand miles per *second*, or about a third of the speed of light. These "superbursts" may be produced by high-energy particles of cosmic rays created in the sun. The cause of solar cosmic rays may be thermonuclear explosions, natural "hydrogen bombs" larger but less lethal than the sort we make on earth.

A recent study throws more light on the basic mechanism responsible for outbursts as well as superbursts. It seems to be vast numbers of atomic particles oscillating back and forth in unison. The masses act together almost as if they were solid things, vibrating elements like the strings of a violin or the reed of a clarinet. Observations reveal that the oscillating particles not only produce radiation of a particular frequency, but also radiation of exactly double that frequency—a "first overtone." The music of the spheres comes in clearly on radio wave lengths.

## GARBLED COMMUNICATIONS

Radio and optical astronomy combine to present a dynamic picture of the sun and its atmosphere. Gas tornadoes and other disturbances on the sun create dazzling sprays of material which are tossed high above the surface and form the corona. Most of the spray comes from sunspots, and the corona would all but disappear if they ceased erupting. Some of the eruptions are so powerful that ejected material, streams of charged particles, pass right through the sun's atmosphere into outer space. But material lost from the corona is replenished by fresh supplies bubbling and spouting up from the body of the sun.

Such facts are of more than academic interest. We are very much concerned with what happens to those streams of ejected particles. Walter Roberts, head of the Colorado High Altitude Observatory, has described how these eruptions affected the earth during a particularly violent disturbance, on Easter Sunday in 1940, when he was a student at Harvard. "Soon a brilliant aurora lit up the northern sky, extraordinarily bright even against the glow of the lights of Boston. Great plumes of light stretched like searchlights from the far

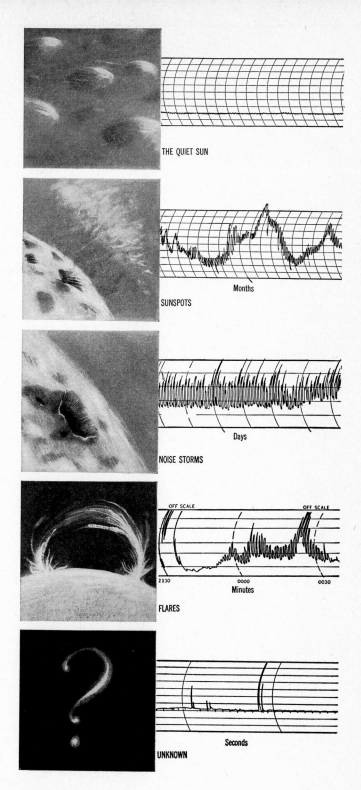

THE QUIET SUN

SUNSPOTS

Months

NOISE STORMS

Days

FLARES

OFF SCALE    OFF SCALE

2330    0000    0030

Minutes

UNKNOWN

Seconds

*Signals from the sun.*

*Rhombic radio telescope at the Radiophysics Laboratory in Sydney Australia; used for solar-burst studies.*

The Crab Nebula, a supernova which exploded on July 4, 1054. An actual radio record of the signal from the nebula is shown below.

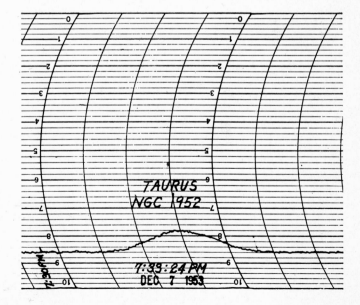

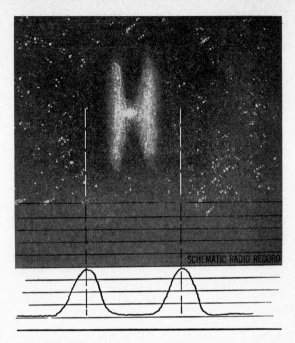

SCHEMATIC RADIO RECORD

*Cygnus . . . two spiral galaxies are colliding head-on, like a pair of cymbals.*

*Radio telescope at the Radiophysics Laboratory in Sydney, Australia . . . this is the instrument that first detected the Cygnus source.*

north to the zenith; ribbons of lights, some with a reddish hue, moved swiftly across the sky.

"Meanwhile a magnetic storm swept over the world. Short-wave radio communication between Europe and the United States was cut off for many hours. Teletype machines all over the eastern United States began typing gibberish. Wirephoto networks broke down. . . . Twenty-two power companies reported serious interruptions of their transmission lines. At the dozens of geomagnetic stations around the world, the needles measuring the earth's magnetic field behaved wildly."

This flare-produced storm illustrates a common sequence of events. Radio fade-outs and an aurora (Northern Lights) follow a solar flare, usually about twenty-four hours later—the time it takes ejected particles to travel from sun to earth. But the first effects came immediately after the appearance of a flare. Radiation traveling with the speed of light precedes the arrival of particles and causes brief spells of static. The static always seems to come while you are listening to music, usually during the parts you like best.

The static frequently spoils transatlantic telephone communications, and radio circuits are jammed with static up to forty per cent of the time. The demand for more and better service has soared in recent years. Static-free transatlantic reception can be insured only by laying another 2,000-mile cable across the ocean instead of depending on radio techniques, and engineers are doing that right now at an estimated cost of $35,000,000. The job would not be necessary if we knew enough to be able to eliminate the effects of solar storms, but so far we can do little about them.

The storms also pose a continuing problem to military and civil-defense authorities. Suppose, for example, that a mammoth solar flare jammed stations in our radar defense network, as happened in Great Britain in the early days of World War II. We might mistake the signals for an enemy air raid, or even worse, an enemy might try attacking during the flare, hoping to fly in under a protecting blanket of static.

Radio astronomy promises to become of increasing practical importance in war and peace. Detailed analysis of unpublished records of radio outbursts indicates that it may be pos-

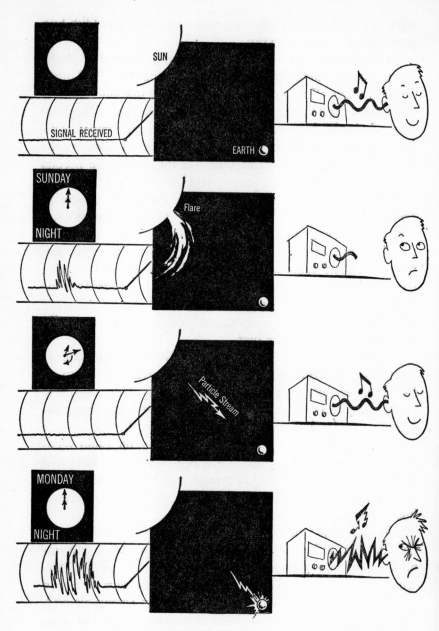

*Solar magnetic storms frequently spoil communications on earth.*

sible to predict solar flares by three hours or more. Certain small peaks, telltale humps on the inked record, seem to precede the great disturbances and may serve as advance warnings. No wonder the United States Department of Defense has decided to support projects in radio astronomy. The new science has now become sufficiently glamorous, and useful, to produce top-secret reports.

# 6

## AMONG THE CONSTELLATIONS

We owe a great deal to the convenient location of the sun. As far as the optical universe is concerned—the universe we observe with our eyes, telescopes and photographic plates—it has furnished clues to the nature of other stars in remoter regions of space. Of course, in the optical universe we can also observe many of these stars directly.

The sun is even more important in the radio universe. The radio waves it emits provide our only information about the sort of broadcasts probably produced by other stars. In the early days some investigators believed that they were receiving radio signals from all the stars which make up the twinkling Milky Way display we see at night. They assumed that their records represented the signals of the familiar and visible stars.

It turns out, however, that our sun is the only star in the universe whose broadcasts we can detect. The other stars are too remote for their relatively weak signals to reach us. The sun is eight light-minutes away from us, 93,000,000 miles, and the next nearest star, Proxima Centauri, is more than four light-years away, or about 25,000,000,000,000 miles, a distance too great for radio telescopes. Our instruments would have to be thousands of times more sensitive. You might as well try to pick up broadcasts from a radio station on Mars with a three-dollar crystal set. It is probable that certain stars blaze up suddenly, producing flares as the sun does, and we may some day detect such events with radio telescopes, but even this is only a bare possibility.

We have every reason to assume that other stars produce radio waves, because they are sufficiently like the sun to behave in a similar manner. The evidence is purely circumstantial, though. The sun is the only visible star which has been positively identified as a source of radio waves.

But this fact raises a major question. Radio telescopes record many intense broadcasting centers in the skies, and if these objects are not the familiar stars, what are they? Research shows that they are unique radio sources, in many cases bodies whose existence had not even been suspected. They are called "radio stars," and the term is used in a very general sense. All celestial sources of radio waves intense enough to be detected by radio telescopes are called radio stars. Astronomers are just beginning to learn about some of them.

## EXPLODING STARS

The nature of most radio stars is still a mystery, but we have managed to learn something about a few of them. The first radio star ever identified with a visible object was discovered one November evening in 1947. The Australian investigator John C. Bolton was scanning the heavens from his Dover Heights lookout on the steep cliff near Sydney. His radio telescope was focused just above the eastern horizon, so that the constellations of the night swept across its aerial as they rose in the skies. A signal came in shortly after nine o'clock, as the constellation Taurus, the Bull, was climbing above the horizon and through the region covered by the telescope.

The signal consisted of a pattern of inked ripples on conventional charts. Although it clearly represented an intense source of celestial radio waves, a great deal of further work had to be done to locate it. In those days instruments were not as advanced as they are now. For one thing they could not be focused as sharply, and it was extremely difficult to locate the position of a source of radio waves with accuracy. It took Bolton nearly a year to confirm his original observations and to complete a precise job of celestial surveying. Measurements were made from the east and west coasts of New Zealand, as well as from Dover Heights.

Then came many weeks of calculating. Imagine the earth at the very center of the universe, at the center of a great celestial sphere. Positions in this sphere are located just as they are on the surface of the earth, but instead of longitude and latitude astronomers speak of right ascension and declination. In their early studies, the Australians located the Taurus source as accurately as possible, and the studies indicated that only one object in that region could produce such intense radio signals—the Crab Nebula, about 3,300 light-years distant, in the Milky Way. Astronomers knew that this object had produced a spectacular display of celestial fireworks on an uncelebrated Fourth of July nine centuries ago, in the year 1054. Chinese observers saw a bright new light flash into the skies: "it was visible by day . . . pointed rays shot out from it on all sides; the color was reddish white." The light came suddenly but vanished gradually, remaining visible for nearly two years. Early Americans may have seen the light, too. Prehistoric drawings on the walls of caves in northern Arizona, caves probably occupied during 1054, show a prominent circular object in the sky near the crescent moon. The object is in just about the right position for the unusual phenomenon observed in China.

It was a supernova, a star which explodes like a bomb in mid-air. But instead of ripping itself into bits of celestial shrapnel, as most supernova are thought to do, this star created a kind of smoke ring, or rather, a smoke shell, a vast, spherical cloud of gas which expanded at enormous speeds like a bursting balloon. The Crab Nebula, which resembles a ball of tangled yarn more than a crab, is all that remains to mark the catastrophe. Analysis of the bright lines in the nebula's spectrum shows that the near side of the shell is approaching us and the far side is receding, exactly what you would see if you were looking at and through an inflating sphere. In other words, the shell is still expanding at a rate of about seventy million miles a day.

The Crab Nebula is only a shadow of its former self. At its center, a nucleus in the midst of the ballooning masses of gas, is a small and faint blue star. This is believed to be the original star whose explosion was reported over China nearly a millennium ago. It was much brighter then, shining with the intensity of a hundred million suns. Some astronomers once thought that this tired star was the active broadcasting source in the Crab Nebula, but now it seems more likely that the radio waves are coming from the shell of gases.

The remains of a later Milky Way supernova may have been located by British investigators at the Jodrell Bank Experimental Station. They worked with an unusual telescope. It is one of the first things you notice after you have finished gazing at the new Big Dish from afar and find the narrow country lane leading to the station (not an easy job on the first attempt, because the one sign provides only negative information, WARNING—STRICTLY PRIVATE—NO ADMITTANCE). At the end of the lane you see something to your left which looks like a giant crane.

The twelve-story steel mast is an important part of the radio telescope. At the top is the instrument's receiving element. Around the base an intricate network of wires has been arranged to form the familiar bowl-shaped pattern. The bowl measures 218 feet across and cannot be moved, although tilting the mast has somewhat the same effect and makes it possible to cover some portions of the sky which might otherwise be missed.

About three years ago Hanbury Brown and his associates at Jodrell Bank announced that they had located a new radio source in the W-shaped constellation Cassiopeia, and that its position checked closely with the position of a famous supernova discovered by Tycho Brahe in 1572. The Danish scientist, perhaps the greatest observer in the history of astronomy, described the sight: "One evening when I was contemplating, as usual, the celestial vault whose aspect was so familiar to me, I saw with inexpressible astonishment near the zenith in Cassiopeia, a radiant star of extraordinary magnitude. Struck with surprise, I could hardly believe my eyes. . . .

"The new star was destitute of a tail; no nebulosity surrounded it. . . . Persons gifted with good sight could distinguish this star in daylight, even at noonday, when the sky was clear. At night, with a cloudy sky when other stars were veiled, the new star often remained visible through tolerably thick clouds. . . . The new star disappeared without leaving a trace visible to the naked eye, having shone for seventeen months."

If the Jodrell Bank identification is confirmed, radio astronomy will furnish the only methods of studying Tycho's supernova. Astronomers at Palomar and elsewhere have looked, but no visible traces of the exploding star can be found.

Interestingly enough, until recently the situation has been reversed for another supernova described in 1604. Its remains, which show up clearly on photographic plates sensitive to red light, consist of a fan-shaped patch of gases. But no radio waves had been detected from the region before last year, when Cambridge investigators obtained definite records in a new survey.

These three supernovae, the Crab Nebula and the "new stars" of 1572 and 1604, are the only ones we know of in our own galaxy. However, supernovae also burst in other galaxies and several dozen have been studied beyond the boundaries of the Milky Way. The big problem is to discover why stars explode. One astronomer's cablegram summarized the state of our knowledge some forty years ago: "Nova problem solved. Star swells up, bursts." Today's explanations are somewhat fuller, but still unchecked.

One of the newest and most interesting theories is the work of Fred Hoyle, a gifted and imaginative investigator at Cambridge University. His mathematical studies show that supernovae may result from the explosions of oversized stars known as supergiants. Such a star may be ten times bigger and a thousand times brighter than the sun, and like the sun it feeds on its own contents. It obtains energy by burning hydrogen in thermonuclear reactions related to those taking place inside the sun. But a supergiant consumes its fuel superswiftly, within half a billion years or so, which is not long at all cosmically speaking.

Hoyle believes that under certain conditions hydrogen starvation can lead to stellar catastrophe. A supergiant, depleted of its most important inner material, collapses like a termite-infested house. And the collapse is of truly astronomical dimensions. A body spacious enough to contain many suns shrinks until it is smaller than the earth, which is roughly like condensing the Empire State Building into a pinhead. Matter locked in the center of the collapsed supergiant is so tightly packed that a handful would weigh several billion tons.

But it does not stay packed for long. As it shrinks, the supergiant spins faster and faster until centrifugal forces take over and it begins to swell and rip itself apart. The temperature inside a supernova is some twelve billion degrees, three hundred times hotter than the interior of the sun. The star bursts and sends clouds into space, vast, spreading emitters of radio signals. Its energy is equal to that produced by the simultaneous detonation of $10^{24}$ hydrogen bombs (mathematicians' shorthand for the number one followed by 24 zeros). To put it another way, if seven million hydrogen bombs had been detonated every second ever since the earth was formed, their total energy would still be less than that released by a single supernova. Such an explosion has been called "the most violent outburst occurring in nature."

Research on supernovae is attracting more and more attention, perhaps because we are understandably curious about any and all nuclear explosions greater than the ones currently being produced on earth. And the skies confirm what atomic tests and the mathematical equations of physics already indicate, that these new forces are inconceivably more powerful than anything in human experience. There are other reasons for the fresh interest in stellar explosions. Supernovae have been used in explanations of cosmic rays, the formation of the earth and the bulk of radio waves from space.

All this implies that exploding stars are more common events than we once thought. The universe is humming with radio and cosmic radiations, and is filled with planets and solar systems. In an average galaxy such as our Milky Way, the one often-quoted estimate is that one star turns into a supernova every five hundred years, but new studies in radio astronomy hint that it may happen far more frequently, probably once every generation or so. Catastrophe is nothing special in the wide expanses of the universe.

## STREAKS IN THE SKY

Exploding stars have been studied for many years, but the brightest of all radio stars turns out to be something never before observed in the history of astronomy. Like Tycho's supernova, it lies in the direction of the constellation Cassiopeia. Its signals are so intense that they almost drown out the weaker signals of the supernova. This Cassiopeia source, which investigators call "Cass" for short, broadcasts at an amazing power level of ten million billion billion kilowatts. It is the strongest radio source known.

It was discovered more than seven years ago at the Rifle Range, Cambridge University's radio observatory, where Martin Ryle and Graham Smith were using a twin-aerial interferometer to study another powerful radio source in another constellation. Quite unexpectedly, Cass came in clearly one evening, writing its signature as a series of the familiar fine ripples. But discovering a radio star is only part, and generally the lesser part, of the battle. The real problem is to identify it, and in this case that meant waiting until a better radio telescope could be built.

As usual, it was a matter of obtaining better resolution or sharper focusing. The original instrument covered too broad a region of sky to define the position of Cass precisely, and optical telescopes swept the region in vain for a visible object that could produce such a barrage of radio waves. So Ryle and Smith constructed another instrument, using two discarded radar antennas (this was the pair of bowl-shaped aerials I saw during my visit to the Rifle Range). The new receiver was about a hundred times more accurate—that is, it narrowed the position of Cass to a region a hundred times smaller than had been possible in previous observations. Now optical telescopes could be directed to a manageable area and it could be scanned thoroughly with long-time-exposure photographs.

Some hints as to the nature of Cass were obtained at Cambridge by this method. Photographs taken with a 36-inch telescope showed an unusual object. A faint arch of light, a curving ribbon of incandescent gases millions of miles long, appeared slightly to the north of the position of the radio star. Fuller details were not known until the fall of 1951, when observers in California focused the Mount Palomar telescope on Cass. A short time after receiving precise position measurements from the Ryle group in England, Walter Baade and Rudolph Minkowski, of the California Institute of Technology, two of the world's foremost astronomers, went to the top of the mountain to see what the 200-inch giant would pick up.

Their photographs, some of which have been published recently, indicate an entirely new kind of phenomenon. Only the curving arc of gases can be seen on plates sensitive to blue light, but red-sensitive plates reveal far more. In the words of Baade and Minkowski: "They show, besides the arc and mainly to the south of it, broken bits of nebulosity of a most remarkable kind. Some are elongated streaks . . . others have almost stellar appearance. In intensity they range from very bright objects to mere smudges just above the limit of the plates." Filaments of condensed gas are found in a region nearly fifteen hundred cubic light-years in volume, spacious enough to hold nearly a thousand billion billion suns.

And the gases are swirling about like the gases an instant after a nuclear explosion. If all the hurricanes that have occurred on the earth since the beginning of geological time were rolled up into a single superhurricane, the effect would be a feeble puff compared with the turbulence taking place continuously in Cass. Vast stretches of interstellar space are the scene of shock waves, vortices, snaking jets and interstellar eddies as large as the solar system. There is an observed velocity spread of more than 3,000 miles a second in the radio star—that is, some parts of the filaments are moving more than three thousand miles a second with respect to other parts—a measure of the degree of internal turbulence.

Such rapid motions indicate that the structure of Cass is undergoing alterations, and Baade has actually seen them. Photographs taken since the original set reveal marked changes in the brightness, shape and position of some of the filaments in the great arc of gases. During the next five years or so they may even disappear entirely, while less turbulent filaments may last another two or three decades. In fact, radical changes may already have taken place. For all we know, the whole radio star may already have dispersed itself through space. We may be observing a radio and optical "ghost."

Cass happens to be many hundreds of light-years away. That means its light, and radio waves, take centuries to reach the earth. The events we observe today happened long ago—perhaps before the dawn of recorded history, before the pyramids and man's earliest civilizations. Since that time Cass may have vanished like wisps of cosmic smoke in the vastness of space. In this sense, all astronomy is a historical study. We are always behind the times. We never know and can never know what the universe is like, only what it was like in another age. We see the most distant galaxies by the radiation they emitted during the early days of the earth's creation.

Astronomers are a bit embarrassed nowadays when the question of distances comes up. Recently, through other research by Baade, they have learned that many remote galaxies may be three or four times further away than originally estimated. Even in our own galaxy, in our own celestial neighborhood, distance measurements may be appreciably in error. For example, when I started writing this chapter Cass was thought to be 1,000 light-years away. That figure was based on preliminary estimates from Mount Palomar. Before I had half finished the chapter (I write very slowly), however, the suggested distance was raised to at least 10,000 light-years—based on new and controversial radio-astronomy observations by a pair of young investigators at the Naval Research Laboratory. This part of the story will be told in a later chapter.

Other broadcasting sources or radio stars in the Milky Way have been identified with strange populations of fragmentary clouds and arches. Minkowski focused the 48-inch Schmidt telescope at the Mount Palomar Observatory on a radio star located by the Australians in the constellation Puppis. He saw a region containing many large, diffuse cloud fragments and, some distance away, "a loose mass of filaments which greatly resemble the filaments of the Cassiopeia source." Cambridge University observers identified still another radio star, in the Gemini constellation, the Twins, with bright and faint arches composed of sharp filaments. Similar systems have been observed by Hanbury Brown and his associates at the Jodrell Bank station.

The systems include streaks and swirls and clouds of violently moving gases. Wherever such motions occur, radio waves are created. Just as flares in the sun's corona transmit powerful broadcasts, so do the strange objects beyond the solar system. Furthermore, the more violent the motion of the gases, the more intense are the radio waves they emit. Cass, with its filaments that have internal "turbulent" velocities of three thousand miles per second, is by far the brightest of all such radio stars. Filaments in Gemini and Puppis have turbulent velocities of only a few hundred miles a second at most, and, we would expect, their signals are correspondingly weaker.

What are astronomy's newly found networks of filaments? Why do we find clumps and wisps of condensed gases in certain regions of space? And what forces are dispersing the gases, thinning them out? We cannot answer these questions on the basis of what we know now. But we can wonder, speculate and keep on doing research.

Looking at Cass, for example, it is impossible not to think of waves and surf on a galactic scale. The twisting filaments seem to be concentrated around a particular region, as if something there in the center—perhaps a vast invisible whirlpool or magnetic field—were stirring things up. It is almost as if you were looking into an enormous lake in the sky. You do not see the unruffled surface, but only the rough parts—whitecaps of a sort, whipped up by cosmic winds whose origins we shall discover.

One theory about the nature of such stormy regions in space is being talked about and taken seriously by many radio investigators—and even some astronomers. The theory has not been proved, but it has not been disproved either. In line with the notion that supernovae may be more frequent than was once believed, it states that radio stars like the Gemini and Puppis cloud fragments may be the remains of such exploding stars.

A new radio star, identified recently by Dennis Walsh and Hanbury Brown at Jodrell Bank, illustrates an important point in the argument. The radio source is associated with the Network Nebula in the Swan constellation. Photographs show shreds of luminous clouds in the region, and the shreds are distributed to form a roughly circular pattern, or rather a pattern of the broken arcs of a circle. It looks very much as if we are viewing bits of the shell of a supernova which burst about a hundred thousand years ago. The Gemini source has a similar appearance.

It has even been suggested that the powerful Cassiopeia source is also an exploding star. According to I. S. Shklovsky, of the National Astronomical Institute in Moscow, it may be a supernova observed by the Chinese in the year 369, and its peculiar formations may be accounted for by assuming that the star exploded inside an interstellar gas cloud. Baade and Minkowski do not agree. In a footnote to one article they remark, "Since there is every reason to believe that the Cassiopeia source has nothing to do with supernovae, the attempt by I. S. Shklovsky to identify the source with a new star of A.D. 369 is beside the point." Some investigators consider this comment to be somewhat on the brusque and positive side, particularly since the supernova theory is attractive to many workers and our knowledge about exploding stars is still meager.

## CLOUDS THAT GLOW

I climbed a ladder on the side of Building Zero, the administrative headquarters of the Naval Research Laboratory in Washington. The ladder went to the roof. As I reached the top, the laboratory's fifty-foot "dish" loomed straight ahead— the sensitive radio telescope that can pick up radio waves from a human body four miles away. In a way, fifty feet is not much of a distance, certainly not to astronomers. But a parabolic surface that big across makes you begin to realize what it can mean.

The dish in front of me looked like a giant silver flower and even had a kind of stamen, a long needlelike extension from the center which contained the wave-detecting element at the end. I walked over to the base of the radio telescope. It was supported by a yoke attached to a twin-gun mount from an old warship. Then I climbed another, more slender ladder which brought me up to the detecting element, at the level of the center of the dish. I stood high on a small steel platform swaying a bit in the wind.

Immediately below I saw many strange-looking experimental antennas and radar searching devices (the Naval Research Laboratory is a leading national radar center). Further away were Bolling Field, a naval ammunition depot, the Naval Air Station, and the waters of the merging Anacostia and Potomac rivers. The fifty-foot dish is a device for focusing—concentrating—radiation. It even picks up sound waves. In fact, we were at the focal point of a giant whispering gallery. Fred Haddock, my guide and one of the Navy's experienced radio astronomers, saw someone looking very small about ten stories down below. "Hi, Ralph," he said quietly.

The sound waves of his voice bounced off the great reflector down to street level. The man stopped and turned around, as if someone right behind him had called his name. "Over here, Ralph," and he looked to his side and then behind again. Finally he looked up, grinned, and waved to us. This was ventriloquism with a vengeance. Of course, the shiny reflector also works the other way around, as it was built to do. It picks up waves from remote places. Off in the distance a heavy yellow truck in the ammunition depot hit a sharp bump on a dirt road. It was about a mile away, but I heard the bump as clearly as if I had been standing beside the truck. Sound waves had struck the reflector and bounced back to the focal point where we were standing.

The instrument catches and concentrates radio waves even more effectively. When I first saw it, it had just been used to discover a new type of radio star. About eight years ago Jesse Greenstein, of the Mount Wilson and Palomar observatories, suggested that a radio source of special interest might be the Great Nebula in the constellation Orion the Hunter—a spectacularly beautiful whirlpool of illuminated gases, visible as the bright point of the Hunter's sword, about eighteen hundred light-years away. The radio search for this nebula posed a tricky technical problem. Indications were that the luminous greenish cloud emits extremely weak radio signals at the long-wave end of the spectrum, say, at wave lengths of a yard or more, but many radio astronomers tried to pick up these long-wave signals with no success at all.

However, the Orion nebula broadcasts much more powerfully at short wave lengths, and theoretically, all you have to do is to tune in on these signals. Unfortunately, it does not work out that simply. Short-wave radio telescopes must be built to much finer tolerances than those designed to pick up long waves. The contours of parabolic reflectors must be smooth and must follow mathematically determined curves. The shorter the waves, the more the hills and valleys on the surface of a reflector distort radio-star signals. Uneven contours may even create false signals—apparent stars where none exist.

The reflector of the fifty-foot naval instrument is the most accurately shaped of any radio telescope in the world. It is built out of nine pie-slice sections of sheet aluminum, fitted together like the pieces of a fine wood panel. Its surface, the entire two thousand square feet, has been measured by professional surveyors and found accurate to better than a sixteenth of an inch. In other words, the biggest bumps on the face of the huge dish are no higher than the thickness of a penny. The surface is sufficiently smooth to bring short radio waves to a sharp focus—and to register signals from Orion.

Haddock and his colleagues, Cornell Mayer and Russell Sloanaker, Jr., had their first success in 1953. It was a Sunday night, December 6, and they were on the top of Building Zero. "We had computed the proper position," Haddock recalls, "and pointed the dish east at an elevation of nineteen degrees. Then we called John Hagen, our research director. He came right over, and we sat back and waited inside the cabin of the gun mount. At 57 minutes and 55 seconds after eight, Orion came in clear as a bell." The signal was a small but definite hump on the inked record; the receiver had been tuned to a wave length of about four inches.

Astronomers find this research of special significance. Aside from the sun, the Orion nebula ranks as the most studied body in the skies. It is the subject of at least one article in nearly every issue of the *Astrophysical Journal*, for an important reason. If the sun is the nearest star, and therefore a convenient representative of stellar populations far beyond our solar system, Orion is the nearest breeding place of stars. Stars are believed to form out of dense gases, and Orion is the densest region anywhere within thousands of light-years of the earth.

Things are particularly interesting in a "hot spot" at the core of the nebula. The core consists of a tight little knot of at least a dozen stars known as the Trapezium (an irregular four-sided figure). The stars are so very hot that we know they cannot be very old. If you saw a red-hot poker or a glowing ember lying on the ground, you could reasonably deduce that it had warmed up recently. Astronomers use similar reasoning in observing celestial bodies. Some of the Trapezium stars have surface temperatures as high as two hundred thousand degrees Fahrenheit, as compared with an "icy" twelve thousand degrees for the sun.

This and other evidence speaks for the extreme youth of these stars. It has been estimated that they are hardly half a million years old, which makes them newborn celestial infants. The discovery that such stars exist, that stars are being formed steadily and continuously out of interstellar matter, has been called "the major astronomical achievement of recent years." Now radio telescopes offer new techniques for the study of stellar evolution. The Trapezium is probably the main source of Orion's radio signals and the Milky Way may contain as many as several thousand "trapeziums," cores of nebulae where nature is shaping new stars.

More information about these hot cores may be obtained with improved instruments already under construction or in the blueprint stage. Naval radio investigators have detected signals from other nebulae, including the Omega, North American Horsehead, Swan and Lagoon nebulae—all familiar objects and all strongly suspected of being places where stars are being created.

According to some theories, another process is going on in these nebulae at the same time. Older stars may be rejuvenating themselves. They may pick up fresh hot material as they sweep into dense clouds, snowballing their way through the skies. Radio astronomy promises to help explore such possibilities and help solve the problems of star birth and development.

And we face other mysteries. Are there stars which shed no observable light and can be detected by radio telescopes only? So far we have used the term "radio star" for relatively diffuse gaseous structures which emit radio waves. But there may be true stars, solid and compact bodies, dead burned-out suns too feeble to glow even faintly. The cemeteries of the universe may contain invisible stars which emit radio waves.

Some astronomers believe that the Milky Way contains between ten billion and a thousand billion of these stars. It has been estimated that their average diameter is one seventh that of the sun, about 123,000 miles. Radio astronomy may help decide whether or not such objects actually exist. In fact, investigators at Ohio State University may already have discovered the first radio star of this type. It lies in the constellation of Hydra, the Sea Serpent, and its signals rise and fade markedly around midnight and sunset. But at this early stage no one is sure whether or not the fluctuating source is a clue to an entirely new population of stars.

A basic mystery also lies at the very heart of the Milky Way. As far as its center is concerned, we are people living in a world without mirrors. We are in the unsatisfactory position of trying to guess at the nature of the center of our galaxy by observing neighboring galaxies. For example, we know that the great spiral galaxy of Andromeda has a dense and relatively small center which Baade calls a "semi-stellar nucleus," but we cannot see light coming direct from the center of our own galaxy. Interstellar matter blots it out completely, and even photographic plates sensitive to penetrating infrared rays reveal nothing. Radio experiments may offer a way around this problem. Australian and American investigators have been particularly interested in studying the galactic center by radio light. The Australians have tuned in to wave lengths from less than a foot to twelve feet or more, and reported the existence of an extremely powerful radio source, "an extended physical object at the centre of the Galaxy which is an unusually intense source of radio noise." The nature of this object is still unknown, but radio explorations of the center have just begun.

This is only a part of the study of radio stars, the part that involves broadcasting regions identified within the Milky Way. Other radio stars have been located far outside our galaxy, at a variety of wave lengths and at great distances. Indeed, it may be that radio astronomy will contribute its most exciting discoveries in the study of such stars. A great deal of research is being done on events happening in galaxies or island universes far from our own restlessly spinning spiral.

# 7

## BEYOND THE MILKY WAY

This chapter concerns the discovery of a radio star far beyond our galaxy, one of the most significant discoveries in the brief history of radio astronomy. This successful "exploration" represents a spectacular advance which can be traced directly to research in the new science.

For some years investigators had suspected that they were receiving long-distance signals from outside our local galaxy, which, for all its billions of stars and satellites, is only one in a universe of uncounted galaxies. But their research was hampered by one important fact. Radio astronomy is severely limited in determining distances. If our only telescopes were radio telescopes, we would not know whether a given radio star was a powerful transmitter far away or a relatively feeble object close at hand.

We could observe individual radio sources and even the radio equivalents of the visible Milky Way. Placing ourselves in the scheme of things, however, would be extremely difficult. We would not have the faintest notion of the true dimensions of the radio universe—or of the potential range of radio telescopes. So far the distances of most radio stars have been measured mainly by optical instruments. The idea is to identify radio sources with objects visible to the naked eye or through optical telescopes—and Walter Baade has done just that with an extragalactic source, using the great 200-inch Palomar telescope.

He has deduced that the disputed radio star is an extragalactic object, in fact the most distant source of interstellar broadcasts yet identified. But even more than that, it is the result of an extraordinary interstellar catastrophe. There are abnormal members of the wide community of galaxies, and among them this radio star, and others like it, stand out as examples of nature's strangest happenings. We shall be talking about normal as well as abnormal objects in this chapter. But the emphasis will be on unusual events which hold special interest for the astronomer, as they do for the rest of us. They often furnish clues to the basic nature of more familiar cosmic processes.

## START OF A SEARCH

A long chain of observations led to Baade's identification of the remote radio star. It all started more than a decade ago, and it involves the work of many investigators whose names are prominent in the history of radio astronomy. First Grote Reber published in the December, 1944, issue of the *Astrophysical Journal* one of his articles based on observations with his homemade receiver. In the course of checking and extending Jansky's pioneer work, he had noted several radio peaks, regions of extra-intense radiation. One of the regions was in the direction of Cygnus, the Swan constellation.

The second development came shortly after the end of World War II. Stanley Hey and two associates, working at a radar research center in Richmond Park, near London, took a closer look at Cygnus. Reber's telescope was sensitive enough to detect a definite radio peak, but the British instruments received longer wave lengths, and the signals of Cygnus were stronger in this part of the radio spectrum. They showed that the broadcasting center in Cygnus was actually a relatively small region.

The next step was to locate the position of that region in the sky—and to locate it more precisely with instruments of still greater focusing power. During the next two years or so investigators in Australia and England launched special studies to obtain better records. As measurements improved, scientists made photographs of the Cygnus region in an effort to find one object which could be transmitting the intense radio signals. It was a long and difficult process, calling for close co-operation among radio and optical observers.

Imagine that you have to find a wallet you lost on a football field. It is night and you are equipped with only a small pocket flashlight. Assuming you had no idea where to look, you could easily spend most of the night on the search. But the job would be a lot easier if you had some additional information about where you dropped the wallet. For example, if you knew you dropped it between the 25-yard line and midfield your searching time would be reduced seventy-five per cent. Ideally, if you remembered the exact spot where you lost the wallet, you could go and pick it up without any trouble.

Finding the radio star in Cygnus was a roughly analogous problem. The 200-inch Palomar telescope takes a photograph about seven inches long and five inches wide, the size of a page in an ordinary paper-back book. The photograph contains thousands of tiny images—points of light, blurred regions, streaks and other markings. Some of the blurred regions may be our only evidence of star systems bigger than the Milky Way. Searching the photograph for the object which might be the radio source in Cygnus would be a hopeless task without any further information, and no astronomer would think of trying it. But the more accurately the position of a radio star is measured, the smaller the area of the whole photograph that can be examined in detail.

By early 1951 radio astronomers had obtained a position sufficiently accurate to narrow down the search. It looked as if the radio star was located in an area that covered only a fraction of a square inch on astronomical photographs. Enlargements of the area revealed a faint cloudy object fairly close to the radio position. Still, "fairly close" was not close enough. The object was only seven seconds of arc away from the position, about one five-hundredth of an angular degree. But at extragalactic distances that could easily mean it was thousands of light-years off to one side. Moreover, the area of the photograph contained three other similar objects, any one of which might have been the broadcasting center.

The radio astronomers were getting warmer. They had reduced the number of possible photographic objects to three or four. But they could not yet pinpoint their target definitely, and say that it was one particular object and no other. At this stage Graham Smith, of Ryle's group in Cambridge, stepped into the picture. Using the special twin-aerial interferometer, he achieved the most precise measurements that had yet been made. (This was the same study which reduced the search area of the Cassiopeia radio source by a factor of a hundred and led to its identification with the Crab Nebula.) Then Smith airmailed his information about the Cygnus source to California.

## WHAT THE PICTURES SHOWED

Baade received the letter near the end of August, 1951. "I really became interested," he says. "Up to then I had refused to be drawn into attempts to identify the Cygnus source. The positions had not been accurate enough. But I knew that with the Cambridge data something could be done. They are still unsurpassed." He determined to observe the position of the source during his next trip to Mount Palomar, if it could possibly be worked into the schedule.

A night on Palomar at the 200-inch telescope is always a nerve-racking experience for Baade. Although he has been observing for years, he still feels excited every time he operates the telescope. Furthermore, each night is a gamble, since seeing conditions are unpredictable. The entire night may be lost because of poor weather, and information obtained by the giant instrument is so valuable that every available second is scheduled in advance for definite observations—and every available second must be used. Baade usually spends ten to twelve consecutive nights on Mount Palomar, and he approaches the work with the tenseness of an athlete before a big game. He loses about ten pounds during every session.

Baade's next session started September 4. It turned out to be a good night. He took sets of photographs of the Andromeda galaxy and of certain bright nebulae in the Milky Way—these observations were part of continuing long-term studies—and before midnight he found time to squeeze in the extra project. He focused the 200-inch telescope on the position indicated in Smith's letter, and took two photographs of Cygnus, one in blue and one in yellow light. He developed the photographs himself the next afternoon.

"I knew something was unusual the moment I examined the negatives. There were galaxies all over the plate, more than two hundred of them, and the brightest was at the center. I couldn't make head or tail of it. It had a double nucleus and showed signs of tidal distortion, gravitational pull between the two nuclei. I had never seen anything like it before. It was so much on my mind that while I was driving home for supper, I had to stop the car and think."

Baade does not remember exactly when the correct idea occurred to him, but the time was somewhere between the stopping of the car and the end of supper. He interpreted an irregular gray-black blob on a photographic plate as the mark of an event that had never been observed before in the long history of astronomy. The chances against observing this particular event are conservatively estimated at a hundred million to one. Baade decided it was a traffic accident of truly cosmic proportions. Two spiral galaxies—flattened island universes, each containing billions of stars—were colliding head-on, face to face, like a pair of cymbals.

That evening, before entering the observing cage of the telescope, Baade examined the plate again briefly, "to take one last look and hold the Cygnus pictures in my mind." In the cage he spent a large part of the night trying to find flaws in his interpretation. But there was something about the appearance of the two nuclei, something that gave the feeling of two overlapping or merging disks, and the notion of colliding galaxies seemed inescapable.

It is doubtful that the idea would have occurred to any other astronomer in the world, but Baade's experience over the past decade or so had trained him specifically to recognize that image on the photographic plates. Interpreting difficult astronomical records, and difficult records in all branches of science, depends in part on what the investigator has seen in the past, and on his ingenuity in noting significant differences and similarities. It also depends in a subtle way on what the investigator is ready to see. Because of his previous research, Baade was uniquely ready to understand the meaning of the evidence before him.

The research had started in 1946. At that time the Palomar astronomer was studying the Andromeda galaxy, and he showed that most of its interstellar matter is concentrated in the spiral arms, that the regions between the arms are practically empty. Then it occurred to him that the very existence of spiral arms might depend upon the presence of liberal quantities of interstellar material. If this idea was correct, galaxies otherwise similar to Andromeda but without the material should be unable to form spiral arms.

Such galaxies actually exist, and their nature checks with Baade's hypothesis. In their flattened shape and general make-up they are perfect counterparts of the spiral galaxies. But they are practically free of interstellar gas and dust—and they do not show any traces of spiral structure. One further fact remained unexplained. Why did these star systems generally appear in regions of space which are thickly populated with galaxies? Baade told me how the problem was cleared up.

"All this was evident early in 1950. Lyman Spitzer, director of the Princeton University Observatory, invited me to give a series of lectures on my Andromeda work. When I came to the point that galaxies without interstellar matter could not develop a spiral structure, and that they actually occurred in relatively dense clusters of galaxies, Spitzer interrupted me. He remarked at once that it was perfectly clear why these galaxies should have lost their former gas and dust. Traffic is heavy in galactic clusters. Galaxies frequently collide with one another, sweeping each other clean of interstellar matter.

"You can see that after all this I was thoroughly collision-conscious. I did not have any serious doubts about my final diagnosis, after studying my photographs which revealed the curious object in the place of Graham Smith's accurate position for the Cygnus source."

This diagnosis, made in 1951 on the heights of Mount Palomar, received a chilly reception down below in Pasadena. After a week on the mountain, Baade descended to his office at the California Institute of Technology and described his idea to colleagues. But he convinced no one. Perhaps some of his associates dismissed the whole matter as a case of wishful observing, a not uncommon phenomenon in astronomy. After all, Baade and Spitzer had published a theoretical study of colliding galaxies earlier in that same year, after Baade's Princeton lectures. It is only human to be strongly influenced by one's own work, unconsciously of course, and even to see things which do not actually exist.

There were other objections. Minkowski had worked with Baade for many years and the two astronomers were good friends, but Minkowski did not believe that anything beyond the Milky Way could possibly generate radio waves intense enough to set up strong signals on earth. It was probably a peculiar star within the Milky Way. Six months passed during which Baade, having failed to impress the doubters, concentrated on other research. Then the entire argument flared up again, as the result of a talk Minkowski gave at a seminar.

In the course of the talk Minkowski gently spoofed the notion of colliding galaxies, and thus aroused his colleague to renewed action. Baade offered to bet anything up to a thousand dollars that the idea was right. Minkowski demurred, pointing out that he had just bought a house and could not afford to risk such a large sum. Baade suggested a case of whisky. Minkowski pleaded that he could not even afford that, and they finally settled on a single bottle.

They also decided what would constitute good evidence one way or the other. If two galaxies were really colliding, the gases inside them would be swirling about violently. The degree of violence would show up in a study of the light coming from the Cygnus object. A familiar high-school physics experiment, first performed by Isaac Newton in the seventeenth century, is to let sunlight pass through an ordinary triangular prism and fall on a screen. The prism breaks the light into its parts, and they form a rainbow-like spectrum. The colors do not appear as clear-cut bands, but merge imperceptibly into one another: red into orange, orange into yellow, yellow into green, green into blue, blue into violet.

Special prisms built into precise instruments called spectroscopes reveal the spectra of the sun, stars and galaxies in finer detail. A spectrum may contain sharp bright or dark lines, parts of the original light, whose positions uniquely identify various chemical elements in the regions emitting the light. Certain elements can exist only in places where there is terrific activity, and Baade and Minkowski agreed that if one of these elements—neon V—was present in the spectrum of the Cygnus object, it would be excellent proof of the colliding-galaxy idea.

Normal neon, the pink-glowing gas trapped in advertising signs, is an inert substance, one which stubbornly resists chemical change. But sufficiently large forces can rip anything to pieces. Neon V is a rare form of the gas; it occurs only when the neon atoms have been stripped of four outer electrons, a process indicating abnormally high forces.

One day in May, Minkowski walked into Baade's office somewhat sheepishly and asked a single question: "What brand shall it be?" Baade asked for and received the bottle of Hudson's Bay Best Procurable whisky. Minkowski had photographed the spectrum of Cygnus with the 100-inch Mount Wilson telescope and neon V had showed up clearly, as a thick dark line. That settled the case, but since then Baade's theory has been more firmly established. A recent spectrum taken with the 200-inch telescope shows iron X, a form of the metal which indicates conditions even more violent than those indicated by the neon line.

Baade looks back at the affair philosophically now. But he realizes that if it had not been for a fortunate combination of circumstances, his discovery would never have been checked or believed: "I sometimes wonder how the story of Cygnus would have turned out if we had not first become collision-conscious via another route. Of one thing I am quite certain —no one here would have gone to the trouble to shoot the spectrum of Cygnus. It was absolutely clear to the experts that distant galaxies could not be strong radio sources."

## CRACK-UP IN CYGNUS

The identification of the radio source in Cygnus has opened up a field for many new studies. For one thing, it gives us our first chance to observe the results of such a catastrophe in some detail. We can watch this event and deduce what may be happening to churned-up masses of matter. The two galaxies are meeting at a speed of about a million miles an hour, and the collision occupies a region at least thirty thousand light-years across. It will be a short meeting, in interstellar terms. It will probably be over and done with a hundred thousand years or so from now, say, about 101,956 A.D.

Stars rarely have individual crack-ups in galactic collisions, because they are so far apart and occupy such a small fraction of the total volume of a galaxy that they do not bump. They pass safely by one another with plenty of room to spare, like ships on the surface of an infinite sea. The real catastrophe takes place in the diffuse gas and dust that fills the space between the stars. When two galaxies collide, their interstellar clouds come together with a fearful impact. It is as if two great black storm clouds, each many billions of times larger than our entire solar system, crashed at breakneck speeds. The "thunderclaps" of the extragalactic cloud collision in Cygnus are the radio signals that the radio-telescope aerials pick up.

Life at the scene of the impact might be precarious. If we were living on a planet of a star in one of the colliding galaxies —and each of them must contain millions of livable planets —we probably would not have to worry about a direct collision. It is almost certain that the planet's sun would not crash into another star. But the skies would light up with the splendor of many Milky Ways, as interstellar matter was stirred up into a cosmic surf, breakers of thin gases, and there would be superauroras, Northern Lights vaster and more brilliant by far than any observed on earth. The sky would look relatively bare of stars; it would be so bright that only the sun and a few of the most intense stars could be seen.

Also, the static generated by the turbulence would be so strong that we could throw away our radio and television sets for a hundred thousand years, until the collision was over. That might at least give us time to think up better programs— that is, if any of us were around to listen in after the two galaxies had passed through one another. There is some question as to whether life could exist under such conditions because of the intense radiation.

One of the most amazing things about the Cygnus crack-up is the calculated intensity of its broadcasts. The galaxies are more than 260,000,000 light-years away, yet they emit signals strong enough to produce loud, clear records at our tiny listening posts in an obscure portion of the Milky Way. A radio station, powerful by terrestrial standards, may transmit at a level of fifty thousand watts. The bumping Cygnus galaxies transmit at $10^{36}$ watts, a number which can be expressed by writing down the digit "one" and then adding a string of thirty-six zeros.

During the past few years the structure of the galaxies has been examined in detail by two scientists at the Jodrell Bank station, Roger Jennison and the Indian physicist Morinal K. Das Guptal. Their studies are not yet analyzed completely, but some interesting facts have already been reported. They used a sensitive twin-aerial receiver to scan the entire Cygnus region, including the colliding galaxies. For one thing, they discovered that the high-power broadcasts of the Cygnus object do *not* come from its luminous portions.

As far as radio reception is concerned, the two visual galaxies are permanently "off the air." The parts which show up as an irregular blob on photographs, and which represent the center of the great collision, contribute nothing to the radio signals we detect on earth. The intense radio waves seem to come from two concentrations of invisible gases, one on either side of the blob, like the wings of a bow tie. The luminous and silent central blob is the part that is at least 30,000 light-years across. The parts which straddle it at the sides are each about fifty thousand light-years across, and they produce the most powerful broadcasts known to man. In other words, the radio waves come from the outermost, thinnest regions, from the shared "atmosphere" which lies near the intertangled galaxies.

The Cygnus atmosphere is like the dim pearly corona of the sun, but there is one important difference. The corona completely surrounds the sun, while the tenuous atmosphere of the colliding galaxies is confined largely to the two extensions at the sides. Several theories have been suggested to account for this strange structure. According to one of them, the whole thing is a large-scale version of what occurs when you clap your hands. As you bring your palms together sharply, you force out the air in between and create an invisible "splash." The air squirts out at the sides in a series of tiny jets, producing the noise of applause. Similarly, when vast galactic clouds crash head-on, gases may be forced out between them and produce cosmic thunderclaps. The same sort of thing happened during a 1954 explosion of the hydrogen bomb. A mushroom-shaped cloud formed, rose high into the air, and then suddenly bumped into a denser layer of the atmosphere. It might just as well have struck a layer of rock. Abruptly, the cloud stopped rising and spread to the sides for miles and miles, parallel to the ground. We may be looking at some such phenomenon in Cygnus.

There is another plausible theory, which Jennison considers more satisfactory. It depends on the possibility that the two disk-shaped galaxies are not hitting absolutely head-on, but may be slightly tilted with respect to one another. This theory includes a particularly interesting explanation of why the luminous central portion of the Cygnus object does not emit intense radio waves. We shall come to it in a later chapter, when we discuss current ideas about the way such radiations are produced in space.

What happens after the collision, after the galaxies have floated apart? The facts will not be known for another hundred thousand years. Astronomers of another age will look where we are looking now, and complete the story of the Cygnus catastrophe. Until then we can only speculate. But one thing is almost sure to happen. Great gas and dust clouds inside the two galaxies are colliding and intermingling. When the galaxies pass through and recede from one another, the clouds will be left behind. In other words, most of the gas and dust will be swept or combed out of the spaces between the stars. After their brief encounter, the galaxies will go their separate ways depleted of vast quantities of their substance. They will form no spirals and will drift, armless forever, through the skies.

The matter left behind exists in the form of an enormous cloud. It may dissipate, spreading further and further from the scene of the crack-up, diluting itself until no traces can be found. This anticlimax, this petering-out, is in the tradition of many astronomical predictions which are a bit on the dismal side. Some billions of years from now the sun is scheduled to cool and then flare up, freezing us to death and then incinerating the remains. Galaxies and stars and planets, we understand, will become cold and lifeless.

But there are more hopeful possibilities, and since we do not know in any case, I prefer them. Scientific theories are not always so objective as they are supposed to be, and a hypothesis may reflect human courage and fear as much as a poem or painting. The future is not always black, even in the heavens. For example, Lyman Spitzer, at Princeton, suggests that the material left after the galaxies collide may not be scattered and lost. His suggestion is worth mentioning, if only to show that astronomers do not always assume the role of philosophical pessimists.

"The remaining gas and dust could gather into a mass," he points out. "The mass might contract into a smaller volume, under its own gravitational force, condensing into new young stars. An entire galaxy might be formed." If this actually happens, it will be the first case on record of a unique kind of celestial mating. Two galaxies approach, meet and intertwine, and pass—leaving as offspring a brave new galaxy.

## NEW IDENTIFICATIONS

The Cygnus radio star is the first to have been recognized as a pair of bumping galaxies. It is also the most spectacular example of a galactic collision. But several other radio stars are known or suspected to be the results of somewhat less violent crack-ups, glancing rather than head-on collisions. The most recent, reported within the past few months, has been discovered by Bernard Mills, of Australia, with his "Southern Cross" radio telescope. Visually, the center of this object is hundreds of times brighter than the edges, but again, the radio waves probably come from the outer portions. A radio star in the constellation Centaurus is also believed to be a pair of colliding galaxies. On photographs the object appears as a bright circular light with a dark band running across the center like a column of black smoke.

One of the neatest and most clean-cut studies has been announced by John Baldwin and Bruce Elsmore, of Cambridge University. They settled a disagreement concerning the nature of a radio source—and furnished strong evidence that it, too, represents an extragalactic collision. Some observers believed the broadcasts were emitted from one cloudy object in a large group of galaxies some 60,000,000 light-years away, in the direction of the Perseus constellation. Others argued that these radio waves represented the total output from many merged-together sources, that it did not come from a single region, but from a vast volume of space that includes the entire group of star systems.

Baldwin and Elsmore used part of the largest twin-aerial instrument at Cambridge. They recorded the intensity of Perseus radio waves of two different spacings, with the aerials first about 170 and then about 1,900 feet apart. The experiment was set up so that if the waves were coming from the group of galaxies, they would produce much weaker instrument signals at the larger aerial spacing than at the smaller (the difference would be more than ten to one). On the other hand, if most of the radiations were originating in a relatively tiny region, the received intensities would not differ widely from one aerial spacing to the other.

Actual observations supported the second of these two possible alternatives. The measured intensity of the radio star in Perseus did not decrease significently when the movable aerial was placed 1,900 instead of 170 feet from the stationary aerial—that is, it did not decrease nearly as much as it would have if signals were coming from the entire galactic cluster. In other words, the broadcasting region was localized at the position of

*Mapping the radio skies.*

50,000 LIGHT-YEARS

88,000 LIGHT-YEARS

*Andromeda is surrounded by a vast invisible radio shell of unknown composition . . .*

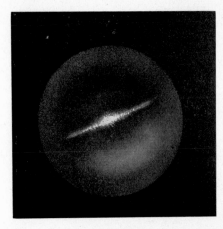

*. . . so is our galaxy, the Milky Way.*

*Fast particles, perhaps coming from exploding stars, are accelerated magnetically to enormous velocities by the "cyclotron" effect in interstellar clouds.*

EXPLODING STAR

FAST PARTICLE

INTERSTELLAR CLOUD

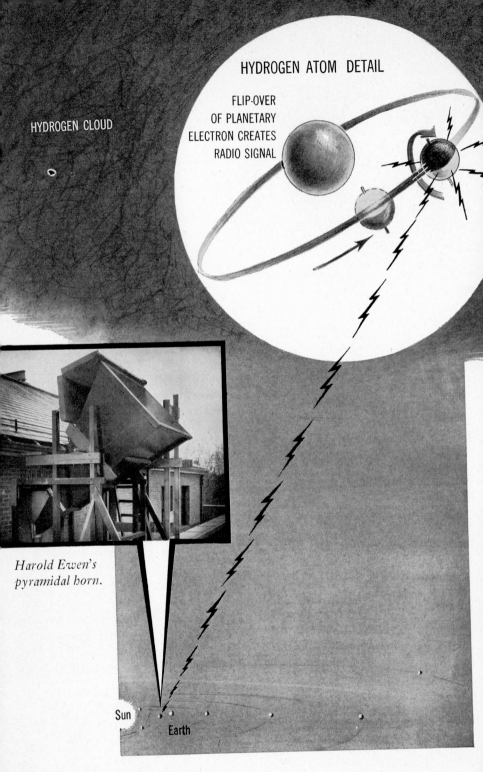

HYDROGEN CLOUD

HYDROGEN ATOM DETAIL

FLIP-OVER
OF PLANETARY
ELECTRON CREATES
RADIO SIGNAL

*Harold Ewen's
pyramidal horn.*

Sun

Earth

*We receive broadcasts from hydrogen atoms in space.*

the cloudy photographic object which is now accepted as the collision between two galaxies.

Another radio star has been identified with an extremely interesting body. For nearly forty years astronomers have known of a globular body in the cluster of galaxies called Virgo, the Virgin. The main part of the Virgo object photographs red. But extending out from its nucleus, and outlined sharply against the darker background, is a blue-white ray. It is a kind of "splash line," a rare astronomical finding. Condensations or particles can be distinguished along the ray, like the droplets revealed in high-speed photographs of streams of water.

This phenomenon is a superjet, a "gusher" of hot gases nearly 2,000 light-years high and 200 light-years wide. Seven years ago Australian investigators found a radio star in Virgo and suggested that it might be the strange jet galaxy. Their suggestion has since been confirmed. Further studies show that the radio waves do not come from the jet alone, but from all parts of a region thousands of times more spacious. The cause and nature of the spectacular jet is still a mystery.

The list of radio sources identified with extragalactic structures includes normal star systems as well as remote eccentrics. Cosmic static comes from an object which astronomers have labeled M31. This is the spiral galaxy in Andromeda, the one Walter Baade was studying when he began thinking deeply about galactic structure. The spinning mass, probably the closest spiral galaxy to the earth, resembles the Milky Way and represents a second-best substitute for a direct image of our own spiral. Astronomers on the satellites of suns in Andromeda have probably numbered us, too, and are studying our spiral for the same reason.

The Andromeda galaxy is one of our close-at-hand models, like the sun and the Great Nebula in Orion. But while the sun is only eight light-minutes away and Orion about 1,500 light-years, Andromeda lies at a distance of 2,000,000 light-years. It seems to be approaching us at a speed of about 200 miles a second, which is not as bad as it may sound after the reports of collision-conscious astronomers. For one thing, the Milky Way and Andromeda will not collide for more than several billion years if they collide at all. However, there will be no crack-up even then, since the spirals are not headed directly for one another.

British investigators first detected radio signals from Andromeda. At Jodrell Bank, Hanbury Brown and Cyril Hazard made a particularly precise study, using their 218-foot radio telescope. They showed that the radio star and the spiral galaxy occupy roughly the same position and that Andromeda broadcasts at a power level about three times greater than our own Milky Way galaxy. A more detailed survey, announced recently by Baldwin, at Cambridge, reveals a hitherto unsuspected feature of the galaxy. As seen through ordinary telescopes, it is an oval more than 50,000 light-years across, a spinning spiral system tilted at an angle to us.

But Andromeda by radio light, like the radio sun, is much larger than the object familiar to astronomers, and its shape is different. It is more or less spherical and the oval portion is in the center, like the pit of a peach. The great spherical shell, a discovery of radio astronomy, is about 88,000 light-years in diameter. It is a kind of invisible halo or corona analogous to that surrounding the sun. Its nature is completely unknown. It may consist of turbulent gases, or perhaps an evenly distributed population of black and lightless dwarf stars. Radio signals have been received from about a dozen other normal galaxies, including the splendid spiral galaxy known as the "Whirlpool" and the Magellanic Clouds, the two star systems nearest us.

We can expect more radio sources to be identified with known visual objects. Every discovery of this sort represents a new milepost in the skies, a marker which gives radio astronomers a better idea of the powers of their sensitive receivers. We have good reasons to believe that these instruments will greatly extend our ability to probe into the depths of space, for the range of radio telescopes seems to be far greater than the range of ordinary telescopes.

But radio telescopes may even take us to the very limits of the physical universe, to boundaries beyond which we may never pass.

# 8

## MAPPING NEW SKIES

Arches and filaments of gas, exploding stars, luminous nebulae, jets in space, galaxies in collision—these are some of the
things that emit radio waves powerful enough to reach our
aerials. A few dozen objects visible through optical telescopes
have been identified with strong radio sources. But the nature
of most recorded sources is still unknown. A few dozen out of
three thousand or so is not a very high average, and three
thousand is about the number of radio stars observed up to now.

Of course, three thousand is only a tiny fraction of the
total number of radio stars in the universe. It has been estimated
that the Milky Way alone may contain billions of such broadcasting sources, and there are many, many more in other galaxies. Out of this stellar population, which may well turn out to
be as great as or greater than the population of optical stars,
we have identified only a few well-behaved and a few unruly
citizens. All of them together are not enough for a valid Gallup-
type poll, a reasonable sample of the radio universe.

Radio astronomy is at about the same stage that optical
astronomy had reached two centuries ago. The universe, or at
least the thoroughly observed part of it, ended with the solar

system in the textbooks of the mid-seventeenth century. More specifically, it ended with the planet Saturn, which means that our detailed knowledge was limited to one-sixteenth of the actual volume of the solar system. The distances of even the closest stars from the earth could not be measured. Practically nothing was known about the stars and the great star systems of outer space. Little more would be learned without building appreciably improved telescopes.

New telescopes were built. The greatest astronomer of the time, the Englishman William Herschel, started with a telescope two inches in diameter and was using a four-foot mirror before he finished. His instruments cannot compare with the larger, more precise and electronically controlled optical telescopes of the twentieth century. His largest instrument moved with the aid of wheels and pulleys, and observing out in the open was often inconvenient. Observing conditions with some present-day radio telescopes will undoubtedly seem equally crude in the future.

Yet Herschel revolutionized our notions of the universe, just as radio astronomy is doing today. He found many new nebulae and star clusters. He showed that the sun and planets are moving through space in the direction of the constellation Hercules—a finding that was not accepted in his time. He deduced that most of the stars within the range of his telescopes tended to be distributed in a plane, that the Milky Way had the shape of a grindstone. Radio astronomers are engaged in a similar project. One of their current tasks is to find more and more radio stars, and to learn more and more about their nature and distribution. This work calls for bigger radio telescopes with greater focusing power and range.

## THE FIRST SURVEYS

As far as the reception of radio signals is concerned, the observable universe contains no completely "silent" or "dark" regions. Space is vibrating with all sorts of radiations, signals flowing in continuously from all sides. Wherever a radio telescope is pointed, it picks up cosmic static, like the hissing that Jansky first detected. But the intensity of interstellar broadcasts is not the same everywhere. There are wide variations from region to region, and radio astronomers are studying their significance.

If you were making a noise survey of New York City, no matter where you went to listen, your microphones and recording equipment would reveal the presence of some signals. You would hear noises even if the city shut down completely, if every taxicab, jazz band, dynamo, dishwashing machine, broadcasting studio, and stock-market ticker stopped at once and joined together to make one colossal quietness. Even then your instruments would register the sounds of restless air as winds swept along streets and around the corners of streets and skyscrapers.

This would represent the city's lowest noise level, its nearest approach to hundred-per-cent silence. Actually, of course, you would always record something above the minimum level— a steady hum combining many different noises at a distance, or a relatively quiet district or a center of great activity. Radio studies show similar variations in space. The skies have their Central and Prospect Parks as well as their Times Squares, Yankee Stadiums and Rockefeller Centers.

We can assume that space has a certain minimum level of radio intensity, the so-called galactic background. But we have no idea what strange winds or interstellar disturbances are responsible for it. At the next level is static, which represents the collective, merged-together signals of many stars, galaxies and gas formations. The universe is filled with radio sources which we cannot pick out of the general melee because our telescopes lack sufficient focusing power. Then there are regions of higher intensity. Some are just a bit more intense than the background, and others, hot spots in space like the Cygnus and Cassiopeia sources, broadcast with mighty blares.

Many surveys have been made of the radio skies, many more are under way and planned. Two of the most extensive have been conducted with the Southern Cross instrument in Australia and with Martin Ryle's big aerial at Cambridge University (Ryle reported nearly two thousand radio sources). The first survey which measures up to present-day standards was conducted by Reber more than fifteen years ago. One of the most recent surveys is still continuing and is the work of a good friend of Reber's, John Kraus, of Ohio State University.

As an enthusiastic radio amateur in his boyhood days, Kraus began wondering about the possibility of receiving signals from sources located beyond the earth. His first attempt took place in 1932 and was not an outstanding success. He borrowed a French searchlight of World War I vintage, mounted an aerial on it, and built a receiver for radio waves about half an inch long. The apparatus was specially designed to tune in on signals from the sun, but all it picked up was local static. Judging by what we know now, the apparatus was somewhat too insensitive, "about a million times too insensitive," according to Kraus. He gave up radio astronomy for the time being, and gradually concentrated more and more on the theory and design of antennas.

The young student built dozens of models and set them up for testing on his family's three acres in Ann Arbor, which was soon known as the "antenna farm." Among other things, Kraus was communicating via short-wave radio with American missionaries in the Belgian Congo and wanted to design an aerial for better reception. This project was not a success, either. But such experiments and the research that developed from them provided valuable experience, counted toward the earning of a degree in radio engineering, and eventually helped establish Kraus as the international authority on antenna design. He is the author of a standard 600-page book on the subject.

Kraus and Reber became friends during the early days of World War II. They were working in Washington at the Naval Ordnance Laboratory, a place which held neither of them for long. But before the radio engineers left to undertake experiments elsewhere, they spent hours discussing radiations from space. "We lived in the same apartment house," Kraus recalls, "and couldn't talk about our secret work at the laboratory. So there was little to do in the evenings but talk about radio astronomy. Reber told me about his experiments and plans and got me interested, too."

After the war, Kraus continued experimenting with new

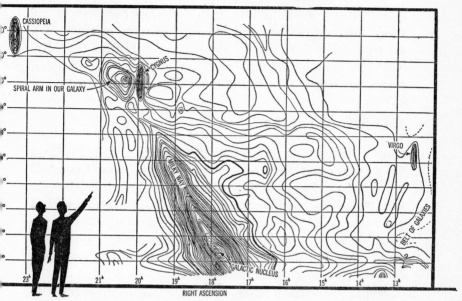

*Schematic map of the radio sky (from an actual map prepared at Ohio State University).*

aerials while he was teaching at Ohio State. A new shape was about to be added to the variety of interesting radio-astronomy aerials. For many years Kraus had been interested in an antenna in the form of a helix, a curled wire like a stretched-out spring. But he never did anything about it until just after the war: "A physicist friend of mine said positively that a helix would never work. That made me so mad that I went ahead and built one." Kraus constructed his first helix in his basement workshop at home, and found that it made a compact and efficient unit which did not have to be aligned precisely to give good reception. Today such antennas are widely used in television and military communication systems.

The Ohio radio engineer went on to plan a unique instrument, the first radio telescope of its kind ever made. It consists of ninety-six helixes, each ten feet high and mounted on a rectangular frame. The entire structure resembles an oversized box spring. The frame is 160 feet long and can be tilted along an east-west line to scan different strips of the sky as the stars move overhead. For more than three years now the aerial system has been used to tune in on four-foot radio waves and study their distribution and intensity patterns in space. Together with the young Chinese scientist Hsien-Ching Ko, Kraus has completed a unique project, a map twenty-four feet across, the largest map of the radio skies ever prepared.

## BELT OF GALAXIES

One of the most interesting Ohio State findings started with an unexpected observation made during March, 1953. Kraus and Ko found a radio source of a most peculiar type. It is relatively faint, "glowing" with an intensity just above that of the general background. The discovery of another new radio source would have been an interesting but by no means sensational bit of news. But this one is of enormous dimensions compared with the commonly observed types.

The source extends over a great arc in extragalactic space. If our eyes were sensitive to its radio waves, we would see a dim band of whitish light, a miniature Milky Way, stretching like a ghostly veil across a part of the skies. We might even mistake the sight for the tail of a radio comet or a radio shooting star. Kraus and Ko checked the records carefully before formally announcing their surprising results, and shortly afterward British investigators, who had previously made a special survey of the same region, confirmed and extended the Ohio observations. They not only detected the huge radio strip, but showed that it extends even further.

It turns out that the location of this source fits nicely with other observations. For decades astronomers have been gathering information about galaxies beyond the Milky Way, and some of their main findings account for the radio records. We tend to think of the universe in terms of stars because the pinpoints of light dominate the night skies. But astronomers often find it more convenient to think in terms of larger units, of star systems or galaxies each of which is a great collection of many billions of stars. The portion of the cosmos which falls within the range of the Palomar telescope is estimated to contain about a million million such galaxies.

Considering galaxies instead of stars, we can obtain some

ideas about the distribution of those in the general neighborhood of the Milky Way. These galaxies are not scattered
evenly through space. There are clusters of galaxies, just as
there are clusters of stars, and galaxies lie closer together than
stars in relation to their average size. The distance from the
sun to the nearest star is equal to more than 20,000,000
solar diameters, while the distance from the Milky Way to the
nearest galaxy is only about ten times the diameter of the
Milky Way. Distributions of this sort are the general rule, and
indicate that galaxies tend to group more tightly than stars.

One of the early studies which demonstrated such facts was
completed in 1932. Harlow Shapley and Adelaide Ames of the
Harvard College Observatory prepared a catalogue of more
than twelve hundred of the brighter galaxies, star systems
located at maximum distances of 50,000,000 to 75,000,000 light-
years from the earth. They presented charts showing how
the galaxies were distributed. Certain of their findings had been
anticipated a decade before by the British astronomer J. H.
Reynolds, who, on the basis of less conclusive evidence, described "a band fairly widespread in the Ursa Major region,
stretching past the Pole beyond Virgo."

This is the band whose radio waves were reported by Kraus
and Ko. It is now believed to include three separate clusters
of galaxies lined up one after the other. One of the clusters
has a diameter of more than four million light-years and is
called the Local Group, because it contains our Milky Way—
together with the Andromeda spiral, the Magellanic Clouds,
and at least fifteen other galaxies. The second cluster lies in
the direction of the constellation Virgo and contains about
five hundred galaxies; the third, known as Ursa Major—Great
Bear—No. 1, is a group of some three hundred star systems.
Most of the galaxies of these three clusters are broadcasting
centers, and it is the total of their combined signals that
produces the long, low-intensity radio source.

So much for the facts. No astronomer would argue with the
observed positions of the clusters, or with the statement that
galaxies of the clusters are an extended source of radio waves.
But the radio observations and other material have been interpreted as evidence for a new theory with much grander impli-

cations, and there is some argument about that. The theory comes from Gerard de Vaucouleurs, resident Yale astronomer at the Canberra Observatory of the Australian National University.

De Vaucouleurs believes that the three clusters of galaxies are only part of a pattern which has hitherto eluded astronomers. His general idea may be understood by analogy with stellar distributions in the universe. Stars are grouped into galaxies, spinning star systems most of which tend to assume the shape of a disk. Galaxies themselves tend to form groupings of this sort, patterns arranged on a mighty scale, clouds or Milky Ways of galaxies. Clusters of galaxies, like clusters of stars, are not isolated affairs. They are merely local concentrations within formations so enormous that we are just beginning to trace their contours.

Philosophers long ago arrived at similar ideas. They considered hierarchies of patterns, galaxies of galaxies and systems of higher and higher orders. Immanuel Kant had some such thing in mind in 1755, when he published his *Universal Natural History and Theory of the Heavens:* "All these immense orders of star-worlds again form but one of a number whose termination we do not know, and which perhaps . . . is a system inconceivably vast—and yet again but one member in a new combination of numbers."

De Vaucouleurs suggests that the philosophers may have come close to the truth, a rare but not unknown event in science. According to his analysis, the three clusters of galaxies whose signals have been detected by radio telescopes are only part of a great grouping, the local supergalaxy. They are part of a flattened disk-shaped system containing perhaps tens of thousands of galaxies. The disk is about forty million light-years across and a few million light-years thick, and has as its central core or nucleus the 500-galaxy cluster in Virgo. The flattened shape of the supergalaxy indicates that it may be spinning.

Where is the Milky Way in the hypothetical supergalaxy? The problem is similar to that of finding the sun's position in the Milky Way. De Vaucouleurs deduces that our galaxy lies very close to the outer edge of the spinning supergalactic disk.

In the southern hemisphere, astronomers in Australia and other nations are looking away from the Virgo nucleus of the supergalaxy and hence see relatively few galaxies. In the northern hemisphere galaxies are plentiful, because that way lies the main body of the supergalaxy. In other words, the Milky Way is moving like a speck of dust on an LP recording. According to one estimate, its velocity of rotation is about 2,400,000 miles an hour.

This concept is as dramatic, and as appealing on esthetic and philosophical grounds, nowadays as it was in Kant's times. It may also be scientifically valid, but that remains to be proved. Most astronomers who have gone into de Vaucouleurs' theory are skeptical. They believe that he is trying to get more out of the facts than is actually there. "We know there are three clusters of galaxies close to one another," says Walter Baade, "but that is simply accidental, a random array of clusters of galaxies. We have no evidence for the existence of a local supergalaxy."

If the theory turns out to be correct, it will represent a spectacular example of ordering or patterning forces at work in the universe. The discovery of patterns is one of the rewards of basic research. All great scientific theories set facts which once appeared unrelated into a unifying framework, and it is satisfying to find that the theories we evolve actually describe the workings of part of the universe.

If de Vaucouleurs' theory fails to stand up, it will not have been the first time that a scientist saw patterns where there were none. The urge to discover symmetry in nature is so great that it sometimes overrides the facts. Indeed, if the temptation to override facts is a strong one, what started as an objective scientific inquiry may end as an impassioned, intense drive to fulfill a hope or desire. Astronomers, whose specialty is all of space and the universe, sometimes seem especially vulnerable to the temptation.

In any case, radio astronomy has become indirectly involved in a theory about the nature of large-scale organization in the universe, and we may expect more and more such involvements. Currently radio astronomers are entering upon a study of the new universe revealed by radio signals, and of its relationship to the old and more familiar universe revealed by waves of visible light.

## THE RADIO UNIVERSE

As a new branch of science, radio astronomy confronts investigators with many problems, more than enough to go around. One of the main problems involves an analysis of the facts gathered in surveys like those under way at Ohio University and other research centers. Preliminary maps showing that radio signals of different intensities come from different parts of the skies are somewhat like population maps in an atlas, where light shading represents low-population areas and the blackest shading represents thickly settled metropolitan areas. Similarly, the blackest places on maps of the radio sky indicate regions transmitting the most intense barrages of radio signals.

To use our own galaxy as an example, surveys show that radio waves are produced in all parts of the Milky Way disk. The weakest signals come from the outer regions of the disk, the strongest come from the central regions. This picture is what you would expect if the matter of the galaxy were most dense at the center, and became thinner the further out you moved. In other words, the pattern of radio intensities corresponds roughly to the shape of the galaxy—and most of the signals come from sources widely distributed throughout the Milky Way.

The next step is to account for the observations. What kinds of radio sources could produce the intensity patterns shown on the maps? How might the sources be distributed? Answering such questions is like trying to deduce something about the geography and politics and social system of the United States from a population-density map alone. The problem, in short, boils down to this: given a large space (the universe) and an ample assortment of pieces, "building blocks" (different types of radio sources)—to construct possible models of the universe as seen in radio light.

An acknowledged expert at this scientific game, which is also being played by scientists in Australia and the United States and the Soviet Union, is Hanbury Brown, of the Jodrell Bank station. He has built and discarded many models of the radio universe during the past few years. Brown was exposed to astronomy at an early age, went on to other fields, and then came back to astronomy by way of electronics. Born in India, he was brought up at his family's country home in Sussex, England. The estate included a small observatory where he spent a good deal of time stargazing when the weather permitted.

But Brown never intended to make astronomy his profession. Twenty years ago as a physicist he was one of the pioneer group which invented radar, and he continued this work during World War II, spending more than two years in Washington, D.C., at the Naval Research Laboratory. In 1947 he was looking for a chance to do interesting research involving electronics. Like other ex-radar specialists, after the war he had a choice of continuing secret military research or designing electronic machines or exploring the radio skies. He chose radio astronomy.

Since then Brown has made important contributions to the new astronomy. He and his associates reported the observations which definitely showed that radio signals were coming from Tycho Brahe's supernova, from the great spiral galaxy in Andromeda and later from other spiral galaxies. In studying possible models of the radio universe, Brown also drew on the work of other investigators. This sort of study is essentially a synthesis, a bringing together of observations from different laboratories. It called for thousands of painstaking mathematical calculations, "books and books of them."

What produces radio waves from space? One of the early answers was based on studies of the sun. The sun emits radio waves and it is only a single star among legions. Perhaps the background radiation detected by radio telescopes was the combined "noise" of the stars in our galaxy. But calculations revealed that the radio signals measured in sky surveys are billions of times more powerful than those transmitted by all the stars in the Milky Way broadcasting at once.

Another possible source, suggested long ago by Reber, turns out to be somewhat more helpful. This is interstellar gas.

The space between the stars is filled with an extremely thin atmosphere which consists almost entirely of hydrogen. Near the hottest stars hydrogen atoms, "cooked" in great galactic furnaces, move faster and more and more violently. In the process, they emit radio waves like some of those recorded from the sun's corona. Interstellar gases, and also the hottest stars, are concentrated mainly about the central or equatorial plane of the flattened Milky Way. If the gases emit radio waves, signals should be detected along that plane, and this expectation has been confirmed in a Cambridge University survey.

Model-making, in astronomy as in other fields, is an art. A model can never be an exact, part-for-part duplicate of the real thing. Even in building a miniature version of a known man-made structure—say, the *Queen Elizabeth*—some simplifications have to be used. For example, only a lunatic model-maker would try to cut and sew tiny sheets, blankets and pillows for all the beds and bunks in all the liner's staterooms. Things must be simplified to a far greater extent in dealing with astronomical models, especially since we have a great deal to learn about the universe we are supposed to be representing.

In his model of the radio universe, Brown uses certain assumptions about this galaxy and others which make his task possible. Otherwise, the mathematics of the model would be hopelessly unwieldy. Following the lead of Dutch astronomers at the University of Leiden Observatory, he assumes that broadcasting gases are spread evenly throughout a pancake-shaped volume about the central galactic plane, a region 81,500 light-years across and about 650 light-years thick. Although interstellar gases are not spread uniformly over that exact volume, this distribution stands as a reasonable first approximation to reality.

But interstellar gas is not enough by itself. It can produce only part of the radiation observed by radio telescopes, and the discrepancy is especially marked at longer wave lengths. The observed intensities of ten-foot waves, for example, are twenty times greater than the output of the gas "pancakes" alone. Also, a sharp concentration of high-power radio waves is detected at the center of the Milky Way, and gases are not correspondingly dense in the inner regions. So, to account for these facts, the model must include other sources of intense radio signals.

These sources are the ones which emit radio signals that come in most powerfully at longer wave lengths, and they include some of the brightest stars in the radio sky. Among them may be great filaments and wisps of turbulent matter, like those observed in the Cassiopeia and Gemini sources. Another type of source may also contribute to radiation over and above that caused by thinly distributed interstellar gases—the shells of exploded stars, supernovae like the Crab Nebula. The very intensity of radio signals detected from the central regions of the Milky Way is one reason why some astronomers are convinced that supernovae occur frequently, every two or three decades instead of every few centuries as was once believed.

These shattered suns would be more common toward the central regions, because that is where most of the galaxy's stars are. And it would be natural to find them associated with older, more turbulent and unstable stars, which also tend to be more concentrated in the center. All in all, the evidence strongly suggests that an appreciable proportion of cosmic radio waves come from sources distributed chiefly in a lens-shaped volume about 20,000 light-years across and 3,000 light-years thick, the dimensions assumed by Brown in his model.

## EXTRAGALACTIC WAVES

The model is still incomplete, however. Interstellar gas and radio sources fail to explain most of the radiation observed at long wave lengths. Together they account for only about forty per cent of the total. A third general type of broadcasting transmitter must be identified, and a study of radio-sky surveys hints at its nature. All observers detect intense signals when their radio telescopes are directed toward the center of the Milky Way disk. This could have been predicted, since they are peering along the galaxy's plane, through a large concentration of matter and radio sources.

But a further observation is more of a surprise—the unexpectedly high intensity of signals received from certain directions. For example, if you listen in at right angles to the plane of the galaxy, looking up through the thin edge of the disk instead of along its interior, the signals you receive are weaker than those coming from the center. But the signals are not so much weaker as would be the case if all the radio waves came from interstellar gas and from galactic radio sources like Cassiopeia or the Crab Nebula.

The same sort of effect is noted in other directions. It seems that part of radio output from the skies is produced by sources which are not confined to the plane of the Milky Way, but are distributed spherically so that their signals come to us from all directions with roughly the same intensities. What known objects are distributed in this manner around the earth and the solar system? Part of the answer may come from investigators at Cambridge. The discovery that the spiral galaxy in Andromeda is surrounded by a vast invisible shell of unknown composition has an interesting implication.

Perhaps our own spiral also possesses a kind of radio corona. Evidence of such a feature has been obtained by Baldwin. This means that this galaxy may have a structure that helps produce the observed spherically distributed sources of radio signals. We still do not know whether the structure consists of thin material or a large number of burned-out stars, celestial corpses whose epitaphs come to us as hissing static—or something whose nature is unknown. In any case, it may explain a high proportion of the signals that come from all directions.

But the galactic shell does not account for all the radio messages. There seems to be only one further source of signals —the island universes of the cosmos, the community of billions of galaxies among which our Milky Way is an undistinguished member.

Now we are ready to put the finishing touches on our preliminary model of the radio universe. We certainly do not know all the kinds of objects that may exist in the remotest depths of space. But we can make up an artificial population of known objects which could produce radio signals suspected to be coming from beyond our galaxy. Space contains a liberal assortment of spiral galaxies such as Andromeda and the Milky

Way. Taken as a whole, however, spirals are not particularly violent. There are local hot spots and turbulences, of course, but nothing of truly cosmic dimensions.

On the average, a galaxy like ours emits only one watt of radio power for every million watts of light. All such star systems together can contribute little more than ten to fifteen per cent of the intensity of radio signals coming from extragalactic sources. To explain the full vigor of the radio universe we must turn to more energetic sources, galaxies in collision.

In cosmic traffic, as well as in the terrestrial variety, head-on collisions are rare. So we cannot expect to find a particularly large number of Cygnus-type collisions or Cygnus-type radio stars within the range of radio telescopes. But lesser accidents, minor bumps or sideswipes, are far more common in the great clusters of galaxies where traffic is heaviest. Here is the estimated accident rate for the so-called Coma cluster, which includes more than a thousand galaxies in a volume of about sixty billion billion cubic light-years. Each of these galaxies has been in about twenty collisions during the past three billion years (not a bad safety record), and at any given moment there are about seven pairs of colliding galaxies in the cluster.

Hanbury Brown points out that extragalactic space need not contain a high proportion of "mildly" colliding galaxies to produce observed radio signals. For example, the collision between a spiral and an elliptical galaxy in the Perseus cluster results in a signal about a hundredth as strong as that of the Cygnus crack-up. But if there were only one such collision to every 999 normal-type galaxies, enough radiation would be generated to explain the intensities of extragalactic radio waves. The proportion could be even lower if we allowed for a sprinkling of peculiar systems like the strange Virgo galaxy, with its mammoth jet of gas spurting out of the central regions.

This completes the model as tentatively assembled by Hanbury Brown. It includes four components which contribute to the skies' total radio output: 1) interstellar gases; 2) radio sources in the Milky Way; 3) the galactic shell; and 4) remote sources, normal and abnormal, in extragalactic space.

Like all models, this one is a great simplification and cannot be considered a faithful representation of the actual state of affairs. New findings could, and will, change it radically.

But models are invaluable in studies of the universe. It was once fashionable to consider them simply as approximations, rough sketches to be filled in and revised in the light of new knowledge. But they are more than that. They are also creative things, products of our imagination, under the control of what we observe. The universe as we know it today differs from the one our ancestors pictured a hundred years ago—and will differ from the conceived universe of a hundred years from now.

So we see a series of universes extending through time and each bearing its date. New ones will continue to be constructed as long as people observe and wonder. Perhaps there is something artificial about the notion of a "real" universe or "the" universe. It may be a function of our own activity in learning. If we stopped learning forever, we would find ourselves forever believing that the latest and last universe was the only one. Our ideas about it would never change.

But we do not, we cannot, stop learning, which means that we should not expect to arrive at a final picture of the universe. As long as astronomy is alive, we shall continue to go by increasingly inclusive models.

# 9

## MYSTERIOUS SIGNALS

Today, a generation or so after the birth of radio astronomy, we find ourselves looking in the same places and in the same directions for entirely new things. The universe we have discovered, the radio universe, is somehow related to the old familiar optical universe. The two universes overlap or "fit" in many places—the sun, the Orion and Crab nebulae, the Andromeda spiral galaxy and other objects emit both light and radio waves which we can detect. But at this stage of our search such overlapping is the exception rather than the rule. The fit is not a good one. Most radio stars are not visible objects and most of them remain unidentified.

We are re-exploring the cosmos. It is as if you had lived for twenty years in the same house with the same family, and suddenly realized that all the time another family had been living there, too, a kind of ghost family of whom you suddenly became aware because of a new sense. The existence of a newly found population of radiating things in the skies emphasizes the extreme youth of astronomy and of all our sciences. We have millions and millions of years of astronomy before us, and the past is very small and short. After a few millenniums of observing the stars we are only on the verge of appreciating the full extent of the task confronting astronomy, even during the coming century or two. We are in a position much like that of the astronomers of ancient times, the advisers of kings and pharaohs. We too are observing things we do not understand, and asking questions and speculating.

But we do not turn to myths for our explanations, or at least we call our myths theories and they have a different purpose. Some fairly far-fetched theories have been propounded in the name of radio astronomy, but none of them endured for long, and most of them were recognized as somewhat shaky shortly after they were announced. The thing our theories have in common with myths is that they are blended of observation and imagination. The big difference is that they are designed specifically to be proved or disproved. In contrast to the myths of old, they tend to remove rather than preserve mystery.

Radio stars represent one of the greatest mysteries of radio astronomy. We know what some of them are—shells of exploding stars, turbulent clouds and filaments, matter churned up by colliding galaxies. But we do not know how they work, how violently moving gases can transmit powerful broadcasts. What processes going on in outer space produce radio waves so intense and concentrated that the signals travel throughout the universe? Radio stars transmit at inconceivably high power levels —1,000,000,000,000,000,000,000,000,000,000,000,000 watts for the colliding Cygnus galaxies, the most intense source of all. In fact, the very contemplation of this sort of power was enough to cast doubt on findings in the early days.

Some investigators found Karl Jansky's reports "hard to believe." These scientists showed what enormous power was required to transmit radio signals from regions as far off as thirty thousand light-years, and they would have been staggered at the notion of tuning in on places thousands of times more remote. On the other hand, no alternative suggestion was at hand. Jansky had systematically and thoroughly ruled out any source other than interstellar space. He had not started looking toward the stars, but was literally driven to his conclusions, after discarding other less startling possibilities one by one.

Now we know Jansky was right. But still the doubts were understandable. As recently as five years ago astronomers of high standing used good arguments to support the view that we would never be able to hear the noise of galaxies as far away as the Cygnus source. As always in science, basic mysteries remained at the core of things. The doubters had every reason to doubt. No physical mechanism known to man was capable of creating such intense radio waves—and, in a fundamental sense, we still cannot account for them.

## RADIATING MATTER

The problem is to conceive of a new type of broadcasting transmitter, which can work in space and may involve matter so thinly distributed that it is invisible. The observations of radio astronomy leave no other alternative. A new theory is called for, and perhaps an entire series of new experiments, which would make it possible to simulate interstellar phenomena under laboratory conditions. Current research has already brought about fresh approaches to certain aspects of the production of electromagnetic waves.

Radiation is a sign of the eternal restlessness of matter. Wherever it is produced, and it is produced everywhere, things are stirring. Just as X marks the spot at the scene of a crime, so radiation infallibly marks a region of activity somewhere in the stars, or in interstellar space. The activity may be nearby or remote, recent or ancient. It may have occurred in times past—in the glowing interiors of galaxies so distant that their light originated long before there was life on earth, and is just reaching us now. But still the signals come and keep coming. Vibrations pass through space, waves which we know as light or heat or static.

Imagine a spider web stretching from here to the edges of space and time, from here to eternity. The web is a vast detection network, a kind of intergalactic burglar-alarm system. Let anything happen anywhere, let some imaginary fly about as large as the Milky Way get its wings caught in the web, and the whole cosmos knows it. The web trembles all over. After a time it will quiet down in a particular place, but on this massive scale, that will take ages to happen. Actually, shaken by the struggles of many caught things, it will never be quiet everywhere.

Space is filled with many, many "webs," interlocking and interconnecting and invisible fields of force. If the skies always stayed the same, if every atom were located once and for all in its final resting place, there would be no signals—only a universal Nirvana. But this sort of peace is as rare among the stars as it is on earth and inside ourselves. Ruffle the universe anywhere, and disturbances of energy spread throughout the space between the stars. Many events affect the cosmic webs. Here two spiral galaxies crash head-on. Here a star bursts and here are great jet streams and here whirlpools or vortexes of gases. Nothing can happen in the universe without making its mark, without signaling the fact of its own happening—and the signals are radiation.

Atoms are always moving. If you were equipped with a microscope that could magnify objects a millionfold or more, you would see dense swarms of particles darting about as busily as ants in a disturbed ant hill. Imagine Times Square on New Year's Eve speeded up like the motion of fast-action films, and you may obtain some idea of the frantic traffic among the invisible components of all matter. This is chaos, a madhouse of violent and unceasing activity, and the prevalent state of affairs in the world of atoms.

Fortunately, we are not aware of all this buzzing about, or we should find no rest. You may think that your living room is a fairly quiet and relaxed place in the evening. But your peace would be shattered if you could see and hear the molecules in the air around you. They are dashing about at speeds thousands of times greater than the fastest jet planes and crashing into each other at terrific rates. Cup your hands together as if you were going to scoop up some water from a stream. The molecules enclosed in that space are colliding many billions of times every second, and all the air in the room is equally agitated.

Similar processes are under way everywhere, wherever there is matter in any form. Matter may appear inert and inanimate, but there is frenzy inside. Atomic particles are moving and oscillating rapidly in all seemingly solid things—inside metals, plastics, wood, even inside your skin. They are moving in water and in air and all gases, whether the gases be inside our homes or in the earth's atmosphere or among the planets or in the spiral arms of galaxies located at the very edge of the observable universe.

Matter in motion is universal and so is radiation. The two are always associated. That is why we can learn a great deal about the nature of far-off celestial objects by studying the waves and rays they emit. In a sense, radiation is the pulse beat of the cosmos. It is a sure sign that things are moving, that space is "alive" and active. A universe without radiation would be cold and dead. The temperature would be 460 degrees below zero Fahrenheit, absolute zero, the level at which all atomic activity ceases. We cannot imagine such a place, which would be inconceivably more frigid and icebound than Arctic regions at their coldest. Absolute zero is absolute death, and this is beyond human imagination, for we are not designed to conceive absolutes.

In the motionlessness, the transfixed state of absolute zero, there would be no radiation. But action comes with warmth. Raise the temperature ever so slightly, say, to minus 459 degrees, and atoms come out of their deep deep-freeze. They begin stirring and emitting waves and rays. The higher the temperature, the more active atomic particles become, and the more radiation is created. This is what we mean by speaking of radiation as a sign of life in the cosmos, and the most active regions of the universe are also the most powerful radiators. Temperatures of millions of degrees exist inside many suns.

We know of no object which exists naturally at absolute zero, or to put the same idea in different words, whose atoms do not move. Every object is at some temperature, has some atomic activity, and emits some radiation.

The notion that steady flows of electromagnetic waves emanate from all things has interesting consequences. We are not surprised to learn that hot objects radiate. If they are hot enough, we can even see some of the radiation as a red, white or blue-white glow. On the other hand, we do not ordinarily think of cold objects as emitters. Yet a piece of ice, for example, is a source of radiation—and of all the radiation in the electromagnetic spectrum. It produces some invisible ultra-violet rays, although not enough for a suntan. It also produces X-rays, visible light in all colors of the rainbow, and radio waves. Of course, the radiation is far too faint to detect. But if our eyes were sufficiently sensitive, ice would glow with rich hues instead of appearing colorless. And if we had sufficiently sensitive receivers we could tune in on its faint and never-heard broadcasts. This all-wave radiating process, produced by atoms moving ceaselessly and at random, is found throughout nature. In fact, the process is practically a trait or property of matter, a chronic symptom of the presence of physical stuff in space.

Since all matter emits a full assortment of waves, including radio waves, the first radio astronomers naturally looked to familiar phenomena for an explanation of interstellar static.

## A POWER PROBLEM

Do atoms moving every which way actually create the high-power signals of radio stars? This conventional process yields a characteristic type of radiation, or rather a characteristic distribution of radiation. It produces all waves, but not at the same intensities, and in the radio range short waves tend to be more intense than long waves. The general rule is, the longer the waves the weaker they are, and the more difficult to detect.

To illustrate the point, we can use our chunk of ice again. This time we shall give it definite dimensions, so we can make some approximate calculations. Let us assume that the ice is a cube measuring one foot each way, the kind of sixty-pound chunk which the iceman used to bring in before the days of electric refrigerators. It emits radio signals, among other things. Starting at the upper end of the spectrum, for example, it emits radio waves more than a quarter of a mile long. These are the kind of waves you tune in when your radio dial is set to 71, which stands for 710 kilocycles and will give you station WOR if you live in the New York area.

But you will not hear the static of restless atoms in the ice. WOR transmits at 50,000 watts, while quarter-mile waves from the chunk of ice are emitted at an exceedingly low power level: about one-sextillionth or 1/1,000,000,000,000,000,000,-000 of a watt. Now consider some shorter wave length, say, waves a yard or so long which fall within the scope of radio astronomy. Again the power level is low. Ice emanates one-yard waves at about a ten-trillionth of a watt (1/10,000,000,-000,000), which is not exactly a spectacular blast. But—and here is the important point—it is still some ten million times more powerful than the level for quarter-mile waves.

This illustrates the general rule for objects that radiate in the conventional manner. Going down the electromagnetic spectrum from long to short waves, there is a sharp increase in intensity. The effect is even more marked for still shorter wave lengths like those of light or X-rays. Light waves may be a hundred-thousandth of an inch long, while the shortest X-rays are measured in billionths of an inch. Ice and all other familiar radiators emit these waves at power levels which are high compared with the levels for long waves.

Investigators have conducted many studies to discover whether radio stars belong to this class of objects. They have obtained radiation spectra of radio stars, graphs showing how the intensity of signals received varies with the wave length to which the receiver is tuned. Originally, like most scientists with their first hypotheses, they expected to obtain results that fitted in with common knowledge. They expected to observe that the power of signals from radio sources increased with shorter wave lengths. This was why Reber built his first receiver to pick up short waves measuring only three to four inches from crest to crest. He wanted to listen in to the strong-est signals. But he heard nothing, and continued to hear noth-ing until he redesigned his receiver for much longer waves.

The Illinois pioneer did not realize it at the time, but he was up against something that seems to be characteristic of most radio stars. The longer waves are more powerful, not the shorter waves. Jansky had a hint of this surprising fact, but his evidence was not conclusive. Today there is absolutely no doubt about the fact. It has been confirmed in numerous studies, in surveys conducted by sweeping the radio skies with the sensitive aerial systems that serve as our radio telescopes. The most intense signals come from the upper end of the spectrum, which is precisely the place they should *not* come from.

This sort of finding occurs frequently in research. It inevitably frustrates and delights the investigator. Science is an intricate guessing game with nature as the adversary. The rules and regulations of the game are known somewhat loosely as the scientific method; the moves and strategies are our experiments and theories. Nature is continually fooling us, outguessing us, surprising us by doing the things we least expect of her. But every time we are fooled, we learn another one of her tricks. She is infinitely resourceful, of course, and we might as well face it.

But we are fairly resourceful, too. When nature outguesses us, when we find our theories inadequate to account for the facts, we must be ready to shift and vary our attack as cleverly as a prizefighter exploring the strengths and weaknesses of his opponent. If radio waves from the skies are more intense instead of less intense at longer wave lengths, that tells us something important about the nature of the emitting source. The main physical event taking place at the source, the predominating process, is not a matter of atoms moving in the conventional chaotic hit-and-run fashion.

This is negative evidence again, to be sure. We would much prefer to know what a process is than to know merely one of the things it cannot possibly be. But still it is a start. At least we know enough to begin searching for an entirely different kind of radiating mechanism to explain the spectra observed for most radio stars.

## REGIMENTED ATOMS

A process in space is creating radio waves of enormous intensity, far more intense than can be accounted for in terms of conventional processes. Moreover, the process does not seem to generate much light. Most radio stars cannot be observed with the largest telescopes, which means that they do not emit sufficient light to leave a record on photographic plates. But even in the few cases when radio stars have been identified with observed objects, the regions which actually do the broadcasting may not be visible. Precise studies show that the visible center of the colliding Cygnus galaxies is not a source of radio waves. The static comes from regions outside the incandescent center, regions which produce no detectable light.

Something is happening which produces abundant radio waves but is not particularly efficient as a light producer. Astronomers had never before been confronted with this sort of phenomenon, but what is new in the skies may not be new on earth. Scientists and engineers have developed equipment which may serve as a rough model for some of the strange goings-on among stars and galaxies. As we have seen, natural radiation is usually a mixture of all kinds of waves and therefore it may not be suitable for our special purposes. So we build radiating devices which emit extra-large proportions of the particular radiation we want.

For example, the electric bulb in an ordinary lamp is a specialized device designed to produce light waves. It also produces the whole range of other radiations—X-rays, ultraviolet and infrared rays, radio waves, and so on. But it emits a relatively high proportion of light rays, a higher proportion than would be produced by less efficient devices. Infrared electric heaters, X-ray equipment, sun lamps, and germ-killing ultraviolet lamps are some other specialized devices which we have built to yield particularly abundant radiation in selected regions of the electromagnetic spectrum.

The devices we build to produce radio waves are of special interest. Not only do they help us gain insight into things under way in space, but they represent a significant advance in the control of nature. Electrons inside the glowing tungsten filament of an electric lamp are moving about in helter-skelter fashion, colliding and bouncing off one another millions of times a second, and we know that this kind of disordered process is typical of most radiating devices, natural or manmade. Random motions of many different varieties are common throughout the universe, a fact which caused the British astronomer Arthur Eddington to remark that "the music of the spheres has almost a suggestion of—jazz."

But chaos does not always suit our purposes. In fact, when there is a demand for intense radio waves we are forced to dispense with chaos. The specifications call for other measures. We must regiment atomic particles, set them marching in formations and according to schedules worked out by electronic engineers. This is one way of achieving power. Whenever you order or regularize motion, you open up the possibility of creating appreciable forces.

Air is not particularly interesting in its quiet stages. It is a collection of countless molecules moving rapidly in all directions and getting nowhere. But set a large number of those molecules going in the same direction, impose a degree of regularity on their comings and goings, and you have something else again. The aggregate has a predominant direction. In a sense, the mob has found a voice if not a purpose. Air becomes wind. It may become a twisting cyclone or a head-on wind that plows forward like a high-speed bulldozer.

Radio-wave transmitters exist simply to impose orderly motions on groups of electrons. They may be glass tubes, larger versions of the tubes used in a radio or television receiver, containing special filaments and other parts. They are known as oscillators. Inside the tubes electrons are put through carefully controlled paces. The particles are made to oscillate, to jump from one position to another and back again in predetermined paths. Move a stick back and forth slowly in a pool of water, and you create a series of waves. Move the stick more rapidly and you create smaller, more numerous waves which spread out in concentric circles.

The same sort of thing happens in radio transmitters. Electrons move back and forth rapidly, vibrating like the elements of stringed instruments. They have a definite tempo or rhythm, and the whole art of radio and television communications depends on maintaining the electronic beat under all conditions. For ordinary radio reception the rates of vibration vary from about 500,000 to 1,500,000 a second. The oscillating atomic particles give rise to the waves you tune in on when you listen to your favorite programs.

Radio waves coming from remote parts of the universe are the result of even more rapid electronic vibrations. They may be produced by particles vibrating from 10,000,000 to more than 200,000,000,000 times a second. We can also produce such waves on earth. Our television and FM stations broadcast at frequencies of about 50,000,000 to just under 1,000,000,-000 oscillations or cycles a second. Transmitters known as traveling-wave tubes emit radar-type waves which represent oscillations as rapid as the fastest yet received from interstellar space. Full details about them have not been published, but it is known that these special tubes make it possible to detect planes and guided missiles with improved accuracy, and will play an increasingly important part in the nation's radar defenses.

Does nature produce radio waves the way we do? Only in a very general sense. Radio waves may be produced by oscillating atomic particles—by regular, rhythmical motions of the units that make up all substances. Radio waves may signal the existence of vibrating matter. The problem is how to set the matter vibrating, and clearly nature's methods must differ from ours in important respects.

We use definite structures, physical rigidity and enclosed spaces to regiment the motions of electrons. First we prepare precise plans, circuit diagrams and engineering blueprints which specify exactly what should be constructed and how. We machine metal parts, filaments and wires and grids. We assemble them inside a glass or metal container in just the right order and positions. Then we feed or "inject" electricity, streams of electrons produced by other machines, into the tube and create radiations of different wave lengths and intensities. In such ways we manage to achieve ordered electronic motions in small localized spaces.

Nature works in wide expanses of the skies. She can achieve regularity without rigidity, ordered motions without sharply defined structures. Her raw materials are hot and thinly distributed gases in between the stars, and nothing else. As in the case of traveling-wave radar tubes, full details of what happens from there on have not been published. This time, however, the reason has absolutely nothing to do with military secrecy. We simply do not know. The generation of intense long-wave radio signals in space is one of the major problems of radio astronomy.

## INTERSTELLAR TRANSMITTERS

But the evidence we already have offers certain clues. Signals seem to be associated with violently moving gases, and the more violent the motion the stronger the signals. Radio stars in the constellations of Puppis and Gemini consist of turbulent gases sweeping past one another at speeds of up to more than a hundred miles a second. But these sources emit signals thousands of times fainter or less intense than those of the "jet galaxy" in Virgo, the Cassiopeia filaments and the colliding star systems of Cygnus, all of which have gases moving as swiftly as two thousand or more miles a second.

Things are sufficiently stirred up to produce a rich variety of celestial fireworks, but as far as radio waves are concerned, high velocities and violence are not always enough. There must also be some sort of order. We need some force or set of conditions which will cause particles in gases to move back and forth with a definite beat. Rhythmical oscillations, atomic metronomes, produce some of the intense, long-wave radio signals we observe—and continuing rhythms produce continuing, persisting signals.

We have many theories to explain the implied presence of regularity in interstellar gases. Rhythms could conceivably be established in clouds of electrons stretching over vast regions of space. The clouds are thin, rarefied, many, many times less dense than the air of our atmosphere even at the top of the highest mountain. Now if such a cloud is suddenly compressed, say, because it has moved into a denser region or collided with another cloud, then the electrons are forced closer and closer together as the cloud is squeezed into a smaller volume.

The electrons will not remain close together, however. They are particles with negative electrical charges, and birds of a feather do not flock together in the atomic world. Particles bearing the same charges repel each other vigorously, and the repulsion becomes stronger the closer they approach one another. So the electrons of interstellar clouds can be compressed into a small volume, but only up to a point. After that, repulsive forces take over and the particles fly apart. They fly too far and too fast, overshooting their previous positions and coming too close to other groups of electrons which make up the outer parts of the cloud.

That means they are pushed back again, repelled by powerful electrical forces. Then the electrons rush the other way, until they again come close to electrons at the center of the cloud, and are again repelled. The result is an electronic "spring" which stretches and contracts repeatedly. Masses of electrons are bunched together and shuttle back and forth between places which repel them, a continuing out-of-the-frying-pan-into-the-fire process. These oscillations may be what is needed to account for the kind of radio bursts which take place in the corona of the sun and, presumably, on many other stars.

But this process, known as "plasma oscillation," is by no means the whole story. For one thing, it requires gaseous matter more dense than that found in most of the radio sources in space. Another type of process or processes must be found to account for them—and a clue has come in a roundabout way from an unexpected observation. Some years ago physicists of the University of California at Berkeley began using a new atom-smashing machine which produces energies of hundreds of millions of electron volts. The machine contains a high-power magnet around which charged atomic particles are made to revolve like satellites around a massive center.

At split-second intervals the magnet delivers extremely powerful pulses. The pulses are timed carefully and applied at just the right instant, when bunches of the charged particles are speeding around for another circuit about the center. The pulses give the particles a "kick" or "push" which accelerates them as effectively as the accelerator of a car produces an extra burst of speed. Millions of such magnetic pushes finally create a stream of superfast particles moving at speeds close to that of light, 186,000 miles a second. The machine which delivers the synchronized pulses, and the atom-smashing barrage of tiny bullets, is called a synchrotron.

Berkeley investigators noticed a peculiar thing about the stream as it spurted from the synchrotron, a phenomenon that earlier and less powerful equipment had not permitted them to observe. The stream was glowing with a weird intense light. In 1949, Julian Schwinger, of Harvard University, announced a mathematical theory to explain the atomic glow. His explanation was that when electrically charged particles attain high velocities they lose some of their energy. The energy is transformed into radiation, into light and other waves.

The existence of radio stars indicates that something of this sort may be happening in space. Perhaps conditions among the stars can result in natural synchrotrons, many times more powerful than the ones we design but working along similar lines. Wherever such conditions are found, whether in the laboratory or in the remote skies, two basic elements are called for—magnetic fields and charged atomic particles. The original particles, which would have to be already moving at fairly high but not spectacular speeds, could be provided by a variety of phenomena. Some of them might be matter ejected from regions near hot stars, exploding stars and colliding galaxies.

The particles might be trapped in interstellar magnetic fields and accelerated to terrific synchrotron speeds. We do not yet know exactly how radio waves would arise as a result of the speed-up, but one theory suggests that the swerving particles lose their energy in the form of gamma rays, intense radiations resembling X-rays. The next step involves a process which we may some day put to use on earth, the transformation of energy into matter. This is the opposite of what happens in the atom bomb, where the destruction of a small amount of matter yields vast quantities of energy.

To create matter by the ton, to turn intangible waves into solid substance, is something beyond our powers at present. Nature probably does it on a large scale. The gamma rays emitted by magnetically accelerated particles in space may

*Radio telescope (parabolic) at the Radiophysics Laboratory in Sydney, Australia.*

*How galaxies evolve—*

. . . THE EMBRYO GALAXY HAS NO FORM . . .

. . . FORM COMES LATER, WITH THE AP-
PEARANCE, NO ONE KNOWS JUST HOW OR
WHY, OF SPIRAL ARMS . . .

. . . THE NEXT STAGE MAY BE AN OPEN
SPIRAL STAR SYSTEM, LIKE OUR MILKY
WAY . . .

. . . A GALAXY IN ITS FINAL STAGES HAS
NO SPIRALS . . . IT CONSISTS ALMOST EN-
TIRELY OF A HUGE AND WELL-FORMED
NUCLEUS.

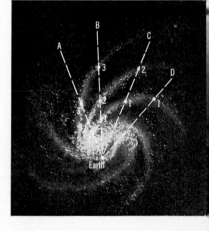

*(Right) Plotting the spiral arms of the
Milky Way—*

. . . GAS IS CONCENTRATED IN THE SPIRAL
ARMS . . . AS THE RADIO TELESCOPE POINTS
ALONG A GIVEN LINE OF SIGHT (A), IT "SEES"
THE GAS—1, 2, 3 . . . A COLLECTION OF
THESE LINE-OF-SIGHT RECORDS GIVES THE
SPIRAL PICTURE.

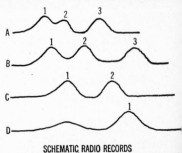

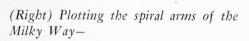

SCHEMATIC RADIO RECORDS

Radio telescope (interferometer type) at Cavendish Laboratories, Cambridge University, England; used in mapping the radio skies.

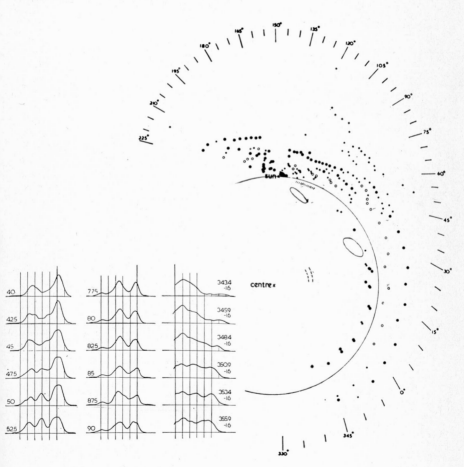

Samples of actual records.

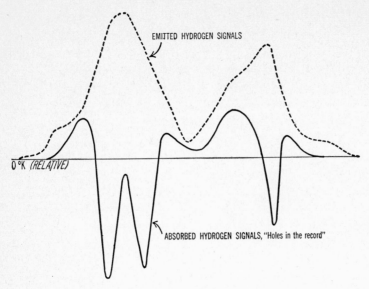

EMITTED HYDROGEN SIGNALS

0 °K (RELATIVE)

ABSORBED HYDROGEN SIGNALS, "Holes in the record"

*Hydrogen signals from the Cassiopeia source.*

*50-foot radio telescope at the Naval Research Laboratory in Washington, D.C.; used in absorbed-hydrogen studies of Cassiopeia.*

vanish and in their place matter—pairs of electrons—may appear. According to the theory, the birth cries of the newly created atomic particles are the radio waves we receive from Cassiopeia, Cygnus and other broadcasting sources.

Nuclear reactions in colliding and turbulent gas masses may give rise to fast particles. In some cases an exploding supernova may set off the reactions, the way the atom bomb triggers the even more deadly detonation of the hydrogen bomb. Jesse Greenstein, of the Mount Wilson and Palomar observatories, made this suggestion at a recent Jodrell Bank meeting.

Whatever the accelerating mechanism, we have considerable evidence for high-speed particles among the stars. There is also evidence for interstellar magnets, magnets made of diffuse gases instead of specially treated iron. They would not have to be powerful, provided they extended over sufficiently great distances. Scientists use a unit called the "gauss" to measure the intensity of magnetic fields, and the ones in space could be quite feeble, perhaps as little as a thousandth of a gauss. For comparison, the strength of a small toy magnet might be twenty-five gauss.

The great turbulent filaments that mark the sites of certain radio sources, such as Cassiopeia, could not exist unless something held them together. That something could be a magnetic field. The British scientist R. Q. Twiss says of the powerful Cassiopeia source: "The internal motion in the individual filaments is so violent that they would be torn to pieces within a few years unless held together by forces which would presumably be magnetic."

Recent work furnishes more direct evidence. Not long ago V. A. Dombrovsky, of the Biurkan Astronomical Observatory in the Soviet Union, made an important discovery. He found that light coming from the Crab Nebula, the intense radio source that is the shell of an exploding star, had characteristics similar to rays coming from regions near sunspots. In both cases the light is "polarized"—produced by particles moving in regular spiral paths—and in both cases such light indicates the presence of magnetic fields.

We are now a step closer to solving one of the central problems of the radio universe, how radio stars work. Their functioning probably has to do with the interaction among the stars of magnetic fields and fast atomic particles. Such interactions may also produce cosmic rays, the enormously intense streams of atomic particles which rain down upon the earth from sources still unidentified. Again, similar effects have been used on a small, noncosmic scale in special radar tubes. But we still do not know exactly how nature does what we do with electronic equipment. That is another job for the future.

It should be pointed out that the Crab Nebula experiment could have been performed long ago, because we have had the proper observing instruments for about half a century. But radio astronomy supplied the motive for looking. The Soviet astronomer, whose discovery has been checked by Dutch investigators, was following up Shklovsky's investigations of the origin of signals from radio stars. This discovery is another significant contribution of the new science.

## ATOMIC POWER AND RADIO STARS

There are still some people who seriously wonder whether such work, and astronomy in general, is really "practical." They are fascinated by the vastness of things, the notion that the universe contains other worlds and other galaxies and probably an enormous variety of other living things. But they put astronomy in the class of stimulating and useless cultural activities. One of the latest arguments against this attitude, which is dying a slow but steady death, comes in some hitherto top-secret information about methods of controlling the energy of the hydrogen bomb and making it available as power.

At one stage investigators believed that the explosion could never be controlled. Now the odds are that it can be, by imitating on earth the sort of processes which produce radio stars —processes involving gases, fast atomic particles, and magnetic fields. The information has just been revealed by Harry Smyth, Princeton University physicist and former member of the Atomic Energy Commission. Smyth is also head of Operation Matterhorn, a project which the AEC has set up specifically to harness the hydrogen-bomb reaction. He points out that the reactions in such a nuclear power plant will only take place at more than a million degrees: "Let us not waste time by trying to think of some material container, some reactor tank, that will withstand temperatures of millions of degrees. There is no such material."

But these temperatures may be produced in a gas which is prevented from drifting away by the invisible "walls" of a sufficiently strong magnetic field. The magnetic field confines the gas and holds it in position so firmly that winds cannot sweep it away. Citizens of the twenty-first century driving their cars or planes past a hydrogen power plant will see an intensely glowing cloud of gas hovering over the landscape. The cloud will be a pulsing, flickering thing, a kind of synthetic Northern Lights display, or a miniature man-made radio star. It will be throbbing with energy, and we will tap the energy to light our homes and run machines. Such clouds will also emit radio waves; and glowing masses of gas, instead of high aerials, may mark the positions of future broadcasting stations.

Not all radio stars are primarily the result of unusual effects involving special magnetic fields. Such processes yield more intense radio signals at long wave lengths and that is how radio astronomers originally became aware of them. The conventional process—the effect of randomly moving particles that is represented by what takes place in the filament of an electric lamp, and that radiates most powerfully at short wavelengths—is also found in the skies.

This kind of process probably accounts for the steady flow of radio waves emanating from the quiet sun. It may be going on elsewhere in the Milky Way, for example, in hydrogen regions near the hottest stars—the regions which occupy the pancake-shaped volume in Hanbury Brown's model of the radio universe. This process also contributes to signals coming from the Great Nebula in Orion. Calculations indicate that at wave lengths of ten yards the huge mass of gases radiates about forty times more powerfully than it does at wave lengths of twenty inches or so, and that the intensity rises more sharply for shorter waves. Other Milky Way nebulae, such as the Swan and Lagoon masses, transmit in the same manner.

Thus two broad types of processes create cosmic static. We can distinguish between them by making a sufficient number of observations at different wave lengths, and putting all the data together to form a spectrum of the radio source. If the spectrum shows an increase of intensity with shorter and shorter wave lengths, the radiation is presumably the result of random motions of atomic particles—the familiar process. But if the spectrum indicates the reverse effect, higher intensities at longer wave lengths, something out of the ordinary is going on and special mechanisms are needed to explain it.

Studies of the varied radiations streaming through the earth's atmosphere from outer space will continue to be of major importance in all branches of astronomy. In optical astronomy light spectra are analyzed to provide an enormous amount of information. They may tell investigators whether an object is approaching or receding from us, whether it is spinning and in what direction, whether it has a strong magnetic field, and many other facts. They have been compared to fingerprints because they identify significant characteristics of remote stars and galaxies.

The refined analysis of radio spectra may be expected to yield equally revealing facts about radio stars. We may expect especially valuable information about those radio stars—the great majority—which have never been identified with objects observed through optical telescopes. Investigators hope to learn a great deal from new research on subtle patterns of radio waves, from composite radiation pictures of radio sources. By tuning in on the broadcasts of a source at all wave lengths, they may be able to specify its basic nature.

For example, there is some evidence that the radiation spectrum of an exploding star differs from that of a pair of colliding galaxies or a Cassiopeia-type formation of wisps and filaments. It may also be possible to deduce, solely from the pattern of a radio spectrum, the approximate distance of an interstellar transmitter. Such an advance would represent a significant widening of our cosmic horizons, since a large number of radio stars are believed to lie beyond the range of the Palomar telescope.

# 10

## RAW MATERIAL OF THE UNIVERSE

Strictly speaking, there is no such thing as "pure space," a perfect vacuum. Utter emptiness is unknown in the observable universe. But nature comes mighty close to it. There are regions where matter is sprinkled so sparingly that nothing, absolutely nothing, in our experience can serve as a basis for comparison. A gnat buzzing alone in the barren skies of an uninhabited earth, or in a volume of space as large as that occupied by the entire earth, would be less alone than an atom wandering through the spaces between the galaxies.

Every time you breathe you inhale about a pint of air on the average, enough to fill a small milk bottle. That pint contains some ten thousand billion billion atoms. For an equal volume, the best vacuum produced in terrestrial laboratories contains about a hundred million atomic particles. If you could take a census in a pint of intergalactic gas, you might find only a single atom in it. Yet intergalactic space is so vast that if you added up its pints and its single atoms, the total matter would outweigh—and outweigh by a thousand times—the collective weights of all the galaxies with all their stars and suns and planets.

The great bulk of the stuff and substance of the universe is the almost-nothingness of an all-pervading cosmic gas. The gas is diluted among the star systems in cold, bleak, lightless and lifeless regions which are the deserts of space and time. The gas is too thin to measure or observe, and for thousands of years astronomers have looked elsewhere. We watch and are awed by the spectacle of glowing things in the skies. We study luminous clouds and nebulosities, whirling spiral galaxies, exploding stars and blue and red supergiants and dense white-dwarf stars, a heaping teaspoonful of whose close-packed matter weighs as much as the Statue of Liberty.

We speak of the universe of enduring stars, of the eternal stars, of the unchanging stars. And measured in terms of an individual life span, or even the life span of our species, the stars are indeed long-lived. But in cosmic terms the stars and all other celestial objects are transients as impermanent as the contours of the earth. A high-speed motion picture of geological history, in which each frame represented a few million years, would show the earth in churning turmoil. Mountain ranges would rise and collapse before your eyes, and thrust upward again. The crust of the earth would appear as a restless, heaving thing like the bubbling surface of a mass of molten steel.

The cosmic gas may be compared to the earth's crust. In its own long time scale, it also shifts and heaves and bubbles. Here in one part of the universal substance a slight swirling starts, an eddy whose dimensions are billions of light-years. Remote atoms come closer together and out of the vortex a galaxy condenses like a drop on the outside of a glass of ice water. Further condensations produce a Milky Way of stars including a sun, our sun. The process continues, and out of the solar gases planets form. One of them is the earth with an environment suitable for life and for evolution. We ourselves are complex organizations of matter that once condensed out of the original cosmic gas.

All these things, galaxies and stars and planets and human beings, are manifestations of disturbances in a tenuous sea. They are waves, streams, ripples, flurries in ceaseless change. Only that sea, the cosmic gas, remains. It is the background stuff, the raw material of the universe. Increased knowledge of its laws would give us a deeper insight into the structure of galaxies, including our Milky Way, and the evolution of stars.

The knowledge is coming. We are beginning to learn more and more about the matter between the stars of the Milky Way, which represents the first stages of condensation from the cosmic background material. We are now studying radio signals from the interstellar gas for the first time in the history of astronomy.

## PREDICTING SIGNALS

A young Dutch astronomer foresaw the possibility of such studies seven years before actual observations were made. In April, 1944, investigators of the University of Leiden Observatory organized a small meeting. The meeting was a special concession on the part of the German invaders. They had already closed down the university because students and faculty protested vigorously against the exclusion of Jews from classes, but they still hoped to win over the Dutch people and made quite a point of permitting the observatory to remain open for research and to hold occasional meetings.

As a propaganda device calculated to win sympathizers for the Nazi cause, the policy was a complete failure. But it kept research alive and made possible one of the most important developments in radio astronomy. The first hint of the development came at the April meeting in a report by Hendrik C. van de Hulst. He had read an early paper by the pioneer Reber and in his own paper he discussed the theory of a kind of radio observation that had never before been made.

The gas between the stars of the Milky Way, like that between the stars of all other spiral galaxies, is spread very thin —thousands of times thinner than a good man-made vacuum —and consequently interstellar gas in our galaxy exists at temperatures of about minus 240 degrees Fahrenheit. At such temperatures matter is exceedingly sluggish. The interstellar gas is a ghost substance as far as ordinary observing techniques are concerned. It sheds no light that we can detect with optical instruments, systems of lenses and mirrors. If we were restricted to the direct evidence of the senses we were born with, its presence could only be inferred from circumstantial evidence. Our knowledge about the building stuff of suns would be severely limited.

But van de Hulst discovered a possible way out of the difficulty. The interstellar gas is mostly hydrogen, and even in the wastelands of space hydrogen may emit radio signals. The twenty-five-year-old astronomer based his conclusions on basic studies of modern atomic theory, which show that a hydrogen atom consists of a compact nucleus with a single electron revolving around it at a speed of more than six hundred miles a second. The lone satellite electron is actually only about two-billionths of an inch away from its nucleus, but that is a prodigious distance in atomic terms. If the nucleus were the size of a large balloon, the electron would be a speck located about 10,000 miles away.

This submicroscopic system may become a radio transmitter. Both nucleus and electron spin like tiny tops, and about half the time they are spinning in the same direction. But under certain conditions the electron may flip over into an "upside-down" position, so that it and the nucleus are spinning in opposite directions. When that happens, a radio signal is generated. The flip-over of the electron has the same effect as an oscillation, creating a ripple in space or a radio wave. Van de Hulst calculated that the radiation should have a frequency of 1,420 megacycles—that is, 1,420 million oscillations a second—and a wave length of about 21 centimeters or 8.4 inches, which puts it in the class of radar-type waves. (Highly accurate experiments performed at Columbia University in New York after the war showed that the actual figure is 21.1049.)

The Dutch astronomer had indicated a new direction in radio astronomy. Hydrogen, whose atoms consist only of a proton with a positive electrical charge and a negatively charged satellite electron, is the simplest of all the elements, and is probably the basic unit out of which more complex substances are created. To observe the processes of creation we must observe hydrogen. Until recently the gas could be seen only in certain places near extremely hot stars, such as those in the

Trapezium star group of the Great Nebula of Orion. In these hot spots hydrogen is "ionized"—it loses its negative electron, bears a positive charge and can be studied because it radiates light when it recaptures an electron.

But most of the hydrogen in space is not ionized. It is electrically neutral and invisible. In suggesting that it might be detected with radio telescopes, van de Hulst was going one step beyond any experiments yet performed in the field. In effect, he predicted that if a sufficiently sensitive instrument scanned the spaces between the stars, it would pick up signals from hydrogen atoms and nothing else. Previous studies, and practically all the radio astronomy work described so far, depend on mixed or composite broadcasts. When a radio telescope is pointed toward interstellar regions where there are no intense sources, it picks up the steady radio noise which is always present in the skies. This so-called background noise is made up of static from matter in nebulae, other galaxies and perhaps radiating flare stars and other types of sources not yet identified. Now it might be possible to select one element, interstellar hydrogen, out of the hubbub and listen to its signals exclusively.

Similar observations have been carried out for years in optical astronomy. Every element has its own natural light spectrum, a unique pattern of rays of different wave lengths or colors which it can emit under the proper circumstances. Prism-containing instruments, spectographs, are used to record and identify such spectra and indicate the presence of specific chemical substances in the atmospheres of the sun and other stars. Galaxies millions of light-years away can also be analyzed in this way. An example is the spectrum taken through the 200-inch Palomar telescope that revealed the presence of special forms of neon and iron in light from an object in Cygnus, and convinced at least one skeptical astronomer that the object consisted of two colliding galaxies.

Radio astronomy cannot yet compare with optical astronomy in yielding such detailed information. But the time is coming when we will be able to identify a number of substances in space by the radio waves they emit. In any case, van de Hulst's report was a necessary first step in an effort to identify patterns of radio waves, radio spectra, in regions where light fails us. Instruments designed for the work would require extremely precise tuning, an electronic "sieve" to select out of a great mass of radio waves streaming in from space only those waves produced by the flip-overs of electrons in interstellar hydrogen atoms.

The problem is something like that of selecting a particular program on certain short-wave channels. Half a dozen or more stations may be broadcasting on channels of nearly the same wave lengths so that all of them fall within the same narrow band on the dial. Tuning in on the station you want may be extremely difficult, and most good short-wave receivers are equipped with special selector dials for fine adjustments. Tuning in on hydrogen would also be difficult, because the receiver would have to distinguish between two signals whose wave lengths differ from one another by a tiny fraction of an inch.

Van de Hulst realized that "listening" to the main element in interstellar space would represent a major feat of electronics as well as astronomy. The broadcasts of most radio sources are mass broadcasts built up of oscillations from a number of different substances. They can be compared to the music of a large symphony orchestra. What we often observe in radio astronomy is the combined effect of many instruments, many orchestral elements. But we may want to concentrate on the contribution of individual elements only, to isolate these elements from the entire output of vibrations. Receiving hydrogen signals is the equivalent of tuning in on the cellos or violins of a symphony and shutting out all the other instruments.

Of course, hydrogen is only a single substance out of many that exist among the stars. But it is an important substance, and not only because it may have furnished the building blocks for all other elements. If we know how hydrogen is distributed in space, we know a great deal about the distribution of the material out of which stars are formed, interstellar gas (of which more than ninety-nine per cent is hydrogen).

Even during the most trying days of the Nazi occupation van de Hulst and Jan Oort, director of the Leiden Observatory, did all they could to prepare for radio experiments at 21-centimeter wave lengths when peace came. But their meeting privileges were soon taken away. On September 17, 1944, the Dutch underground organized a national railroad strike, timed to coincide with the Battle of Arnhem and hamper the enemy's activities. The gamble failed. The Allies lost the battle and the Nazis retaliated against the strikers and the people in general. There was a severe famine in Holland that winter. Gatherings of all sorts were strictly forbidden and most Dutchmen, including Oort, went into hiding.

Secret meetings were held near the observatory. The enemy could no more put a total end to talks about astronomy than they could to liberation plans. But van de Hulst's theoretical work was not confirmed experimentally until some years after the war, in another country which the invaders had never reached.

## A SPECIAL RECEIVER

During the winter of 1950-51 students passing the Lyman Physics Laboratory at Harvard University noticed a peculiar-looking structure. It was sticking out of a top-floor window and resembled a giant old-fashioned hearing trumpet. Tilted up at an angle, its wide funnel-like opening was pointing toward the sky. Whatever it was, it made an inviting target and students stopped from time to time to lob snowballs in. On several occasions they were joined by a faculty member who knew the precise purpose of the "hearing trumpet" and threw his share of snowballs. He was Edward Purcell, a leading professor of physics who was soon to be awarded a Nobel Prize for his investigations into microwave theory and atomic structure.

More than a year before, Purcell had given some advice to a graduate student in search of a Ph.D. degree in physics. Why not try to tune in on radio waves from interstellar hydrogen? The job, if it could be done at all, could be done quickly as compared with the average Ph.D. project. Not only that, but it would be a spectacular advance in radio astronomy. It would establish the student's reputation and start him off on a productive career. "In fact," Purcell pointed out, "if you suc-

ceed you are almost sure to make the pages of *Life* magazine."
And that, by the way, was exactly what happened.

It was an all-or-nothing chance at the time. It would either
work or fail entirely. In any case, the answer would be clean-
cut. The project appealed to the student, an Amherst alumnus
taking postgraduate courses at Harvard under the G.I. Bill
of Rights. Harold Ewen has been interested in getting places
fast ever since the late 1930's when he started racing Model-A
Fords. He has a special flair for tuning up engines and for getting all sorts of temperamental devices to work properly. As
a radar officer in the navy during the war, and later at the
Radiation Laboratory of the Massachusetts Institute of Technology, he applied his talents with notable success to the design of electronic instruments, undoubtedly the most temperamental devices ever fashioned by man.

The "hearing trumpet" represented Ewen's most complex
and brilliant piece of equipment to date. Among scientists it
is known as a pyramidal horn, a type of radio antenna long
used in experimental studies. (And among astronomers Ewen
has been referred to as the "Young Man with a Horn.") The
large funnel which extended out of the window narrowed
down to a slender channel or wave guide inside the laboratory.
This system was not intended to catch occasional snowballs
or rain, which came more frequently. In fact, during one
spell of bad weather so much rain flowed into the laboratory
that it had to be collected in a five-gallon jug. "I was running a
rainfall gauge instead of a radio telescope," Ewen told me.

Funnel and wave guide were designed to catch 21-
centimeter radio waves, for such short waves flow and can be
collected as if they were indeed fluids and not invisible radiations. The wave guide brings the radiations into the
electronic units of the instrument, and this is the point where
special finesse was called for. It is no trouble at all to trap
waves from interstellar hydrogen, but it is a major feat to
transform them into clear signals. One of the difficulties involves certain basic facts about how the signals are produced
in the first place.

When the satellite electron of hydrogen is spinning in the
same direction as the nucleus, conditions are ripe for a pos-

sible atomic broadcast. Radio waves are emitted the instant
the electron flips over on its axis, so that it and the nucleus
now spin in opposite directions. Such flip-overs are spontane-
ous events, which means they happen for reasons unknown to
us. But we do know what makes electrons take on their former
spin so that they can emit radio waves again. An electron, like
an automobile, will not turn turtle without due cause—and in
both cases the cause is a collision. Collisions are extremely rare
events in the near-emptinesses of interstellar space. Atoms are
so few and far between that the chance of a crack-up is little
better than the chance of two camels bumping head-on in the
Sahara Desert.

(*Author's note.* One astronomer checking the above analogy
had this to say: "I like your picture of camels wandering all
over the Sahara Desert, but are you sure that their motions
are purely random? My impression is that camels follow
rather definite paths across the desert and that, because of the
love of one camel for its fellow-camels, the bumping of camel's
heads in the desert is a much more frequent occurrence than
would be the case if their motions were purely random.")

This is why Harold Ewen had special problems in the design of his radio telescopes. Infrequent collisions mean that
only a small number of radio waves is generated, and the signals received on earth will be feeble, many times more feeble
than a distant station on a radio loudspeaker. After all, a few
automobiles scattered over a wide area rarely collide and
make little noise, and the same thing goes for atomic particles.
In interstellar space a hydrogen atom is an average of about
three-eighths of an inch away from its nearest neighbor.

That may not seem like much of a distance, but three-
eighths of an inch is about a hundred and twenty million
times the diameter of the hydrogen atom. If your nearest
neighbor were as proportionately far away, you would be
rather lonely. He would be floating somewhere in space more
than forty-eight thousand miles away. Also, hydrogen atoms
travel very slowly between the stars. They move at speeds of
three miles a second, a snail's pace in the atomic world, in
which the real speedsters move thousands of miles in that
time. Collisions are rare because of the combination of low

speeds and great separating distances. Moreover, every accident does not result in the flip-over of an electron. Some merely shake up the two atoms and cause no permanent changes.

It all adds up to the following statistic. A hydrogen atom gets into a productive collision with another particle—that is, a collision which results in an emitted radio wave—about once every 233 years, according to latest estimates. On the average, atoms colliding today are experiencing their first crack-up since the days of the Salem witch trials in the late seventeenth century. They will not bump again until 2189 A.D. The total power of all the 21-centimeter radiation falling on the surface of the earth is only one or two watts, less than half the power of a single flashlight battery. Since a radio telescope is located on a tiny plot of land, it must detect signals with as little energy as one billion billionth of a watt.

Ewen's original telescope could not be moved. It remained in position while the constellations passed overhead, and automatically performed a rapid series of measurements and comparisons. In effect it scanned a portion of sky at two wave lengths, at 21 centimeters and at some different wave length —say, 21.02 centimeters. At the slightly longer wave length, the instrument registers the intensity of the galactic background radiation. But when it is tuned to 21 centimeters, or the exact wave length emitted by hydrogen atoms, it registers the galactic background *plus* the extra intensity of hydrogen. The difference between the intensities at 21 centimeters and the other wave length is the strength of the hydrogen signal.

The instrument had many other special features. For one thing, it included circuits capable of distinguishing the faint high "note" of hydrogen in space from the crackling, roaring "set noise" produced by the electrons of its own vacuum tubes, a noise hundreds of times louder than the signal itself. Another less spectacular but equally necessary feature, which Ewen soon added, was a trap door to cover the open end of the wave-gathering horn and keep out rain and snowballs. The most effective model of this supersensitive receiver was completed and ready for action early in 1951.

## HYDROGEN BROADCASTS

Radio signals from interstellar hydrogen were first detected at about two-thirty on the morning of March 25. They showed up in the usual form, a rise or hump marked on a moving strip of chart paper. But the first signal was not a sharp peak which could be seen easily from a quick glance at the record. The rise was slight and exceedingly slow. In fact, Ewen had to roll the chart out full length, all seven feet of it, and sight along the inked line before he could notice the slight slope of the hump that meant an increase in radio intensity. If those first signals had been fed into a loudspeaker, the increase in volume would have been much too small to detect with the unaided ear.

But the charts furnished definite evidence. Ewen stayed up for sixty consecutive hours, adjusting his equipment and obtaining an even better record next morning. Purcell, hearing the news, telephoned radar experts at M.I.T. just to make doubly sure that the discovery was the real thing. Were any radar sets or experimental instruments transmitting radio waves in the 21-centimeter band? A check-up revealed that the channels in this part of the microwave spectrum had been relatively quiet in the Cambridge area. The signals were not man-made. Only interstellar space was broadcasting at that wave length.

Radio waves had been detected from a great gas cloud lying toward the center of the Milky Way and probably at least five thousand light-years away. The new experiment, and many others which were to come later, indicated the presence of extra-strong signals coming from the emptiest parts of the skies. The intensity of general signals from the galaxy increases with increasing wave length, and increases steadily and fairly regularly. But there is an unusually sharp rise in intensity, a burst of radio energy at about 21 centimeters. The effect can be traced to the added contribution from interstellar hydrogen.

All these results had been predicted seven years before, and the man who did the predicting happened to be at Harvard when the discovery was made. Van de Hulst was visiting the Harvard College Observatory as guest lecturer, and Ewen showed him the records within a few hours after signals were first picked up. The Dutch astronomer immediately put through a transatlantic call to Leiden, where his colleagues were working on a new radio telescope designed especially to tune in on hydrogen waves. This instrument was being built because of an accident which had occurred the previous spring. A technician had left the old telescope alone for a few minutes, and when he came back nothing was left but a smoldering mass of burned equipment. A fire of mysterious origin had swept through the laboratory, destroying two years of effort.

But the new telescope was nearly finished when Dutch investigators received van de Hulst's long-distance call. Eleven weeks later they completed the job and confirmed Ewen's findings. The Australians, who were also notified, had made no plans for a 21-centimeter instrument, but they put a special group on the project and set what will probably stand for some time as a speed record for construction in radio astronomy. Within three months they built a receiver, "went on the air" and also confirmed the American findings.

Speaking of speed records, Harold Ewen may well have set one of his own. He finished his Ph.D. thesis, "Radiation from Galactic Hydrogen at 1,420 Megacycles per Second," in just a bit under three days. His report marked the beginning of a new branch of experimental astronomy. The development was followed by accelerated research programs in Holland and Australia, and its significance was first brought home to astronomers in general in a paper delivered by Oort before the American Astronomical Society in December, 1951. This paper represents the first official and formal recognition by a leading astronomer of the importance of the entire field of radio studies. It marks the time when the young science became a respectable part of astronomy.

Never before had investigators been able to observe the raw material of the stars. The new sense organs, radio telescopes, detect oscillations which make no impression on the human nervous system.

If our eyes could not see the clouds above the earth, the skies would be highly uninteresting, and would tell us even less than they do now about tomorrow's weather. They would be barren of dark storm clouds, puffs of white, and all the other shapes and forms that drift through the atmosphere. In such a world the discovery of a way of observing the skies would be an event of major importance. Clouds could be detected at a distance, and tracked like remote aircraft by radar sets. They could be followed and measured and mapped. Careful long-term studies of their comings and goings would bring fresh information about the behavior of the upper atmosphere. Weather forecasting would be placed on a more scientific basis, as new facts were revealed about currents and waves and whirlpools in the ocean of air that envelops the earth.

That ocean can be compared to the vast stretches of material in the regions among the stars of the Milky Way. We are just beginning to probe the depths and measure the tides of interstellar gases, to detect and map great superclouds which condense, not into rain or snow, but into star clusters and solar systems. These clouds are now visible to us in the radio skies. They inform us of their presence by hydrogen signals, the results of spinning electrons turned topsy-turvy. The next chapter describes something of the new Milky Way galaxy, a radio galaxy seen by the invisible light of 21-centimeter hydrogen waves.

# 11

## EXPLORING OUR GALAXY

Research, like all forms of learning, may be a lonely occupation and many of its outposts are lonely places. About two years ago I visited a wasteland near the town of Kootwijk (pronounced "coat-wike"), in central Holland. Walking toward a small hill, I saw an unusual structure silhouetted against the evening sky, a structure that might be taken as the trademark of radio astronomy. It was a paraboloid radio telescope used by the Leiden Observatory, another giant electronic searchlight twenty-five feet in diameter and looming more than three stories high.

At the top of the hill I looked around at a darkening landscape of sand dunes and scrub pines, and at a strange forest of steel trees. The radio telescope was located at the edge of the steel forest, more than a hundred tall towers which have nothing to do with the stars. They are the property of the Netherlands Post and Telegraph Service. They are broadcasting antennas, transmitting messages to all parts of the world and forming an important link in the international chain of radio-telephone communications. This is the field to which the discoverer of radio waves from space, Karl Jansky, devoted his life.

The searchlight aerial was not originally designed for radio astronomy. German dirigible engineers who made the *Graf Zeppelin* built it, and many similar aerials, for strictly military purposes. During World War II it stood on an island off the northern coast of Holland as a part of the network of radar detectors that made up the Atlantic Wall, the Nazis' unsuccessful defenses against the D-Day invasion. More than a year after the war the aerial, half buried in sand, was retrieved and given to the Leiden Observatory. When I saw it, it was being used in a unique survey.

The aerial and a cabin containing the radio receiver were raised above ground level, mounted on concrete pilings. I climbed an iron ladder to enter the cabin and meet C. Alex Muller, the electronics expert who designed the radio equipment inside and who works with Oort and van de Hulst. The telescope runs continuously, day and night. Muller walked to a corner of the cabin, bent down and turned a crank near the floor. I felt the cabin jolt a bit as it and the aerial rotated a little to the side. Muller turned a second crank and the aerial tilted slightly higher above the horizon.

Similar adjustments had been made by hand every two and a half minutes, twenty-four hours a day, for nearly two years. The telescope was scanning the skies systematically, section by section, in the plane of the Milky Way—picking up signals from interstellar hydrogen. New hydrogen observations are also being made in Australia, England, France, Sweden, the Soviet Union and the United States, but for many months the investigators at the Kootwijk station were practically alone in exploiting the astronomical implications of this important branch of radio research.

The story of what they found already stands as one of the high points in modern astronomy. Pioneer radio studies, combined with the evidence of years of work with conventional telescopes, have resulted in an exciting and unexpected new development. Alex Muller's radio telescope has been used to plot the remote structure of the Milky Way—the first survey of its kind ever undertaken. It has furnished the first direct image of our own galaxy, a great composite "photograph" taken in the light of 21-centimeter hydrogen waves.

## THE OBSCURING DUST

The Andromeda galaxy, one of the first star systems to be identified as a radio source, can be seen with the naked eye. It appears in the night skies as a faint and uninteresting smudge of light. Viewed through the Palomar telescope and photographed on special film, however, it is one of the most spectacular of all astronomical objects. Its nucleus is a huge flattened mass which has been described as a "heap of pepper." The pepper grains are individual stars, billions of them, the most conspicuous being red giants shining with the intensity of two hundred suns.

But even this display is tame and pale compared to what is going on in the seething, tempestuous regions outside the nucleus. Extending from the nucleus are chains of the brightest stars known to astronomy, blue supergiants whose light may be hundreds of times more intense than that of the central red stars. The supergiants are strung out one after the other in gracefully curving lines, like rows of lamps marking the courses of celestial highways. Indeed, you can see the highways. Along each one of the rows is a dark lane of dust and gas lit up by the blue supergiants themselves, illuminated from behind like a silhouetted profile.

Andromeda's highways are great spiral arms winding around the galactic center. The entire system looks like a whirlpool of gases or the spiral pattern around a Fourth of July pinwheel. The overwhelming impression is one of motion—spinning, twisting, cyclonic motion. But we see no changes through our telescopes, and this fact, more than any set of figures, indicates the enormous distances and dimensions of the galaxy. The arms are moving faster than our fastest jet planes or rockets. But they are so far away and so vast that we shall have to wait thousands of years to obtain photographs which, when compared with the photographs of today, will reveal appreciable changes.

Our galaxy is probably a whirling star system of the same sort. Its spiral arms must wind and swirl through space in a manner as spectacular as those of Andromeda. Yet we know far more about the Andromeda spirals, which lie some two million light-years away. We have not been able to make out the detailed spiral patterns of the Milky Way, and have obtained some notion of their general features only with the greatest difficulty. As recently as five or six years ago, before radio signals were detected from interstellar hydrogen, the prospects of gaining further significant information seemed exceedingly remote.

We have found it most difficult to see ourselves as others might see us. For one thing, we are too close to our galaxy to view it as a whole. Bart Bok, a leading authority on the Milky Way and co-director with Harold Ewen of the Harvard College Observatory's radio-astronomy program, describes the problem in these words: "It is much simpler to obtain a general impression of the arrangement of a large city from a plane flying overhead at 10,000 feet than from a prison somewhere near the center of the town, or, even worse, from one in the suburbs." But this is only part of the trouble. As Bok points out, the analogy would be more precise if you think in terms of a suburban prison enveloped in a thick fog.

Between us and most of the rest of our galaxy lies a curtain of darkness which shuts out light as effectively as a blindfold over our eyes. The curtain never lifts. If our species were content to wait, to accept things incuriously and placidly as we find them, we would have no conception of the full splendor of the pageant taking place so near our observing posts. For millenniums we thought we were scanning the heavens in all their glory. Now we realize that we were looking at fragments only, that we really had little idea of the nature of our universe. We have been like explorers straining to catch a glimpse of distant and magnificent mountains, in an unending dust storm.

If you could view the spinning disk which is the Milky Way edge-on at a distance, you might mistake it for a flying saucer. The disk is a hundred thousand light-years across and only two to three thousand light-years thick, except for a central bulge which marks the position of the nucleus. The sun lies inside the disk, a bit nearer to the top than the bottom and out toward the rim, some twenty-six thousand light-years from the nucleus. We probe this galaxy from the earth—a spinning, circling, wobbling platform in an off-center position and surrounded by an annoyingly unpredictable atmosphere that spoils seeing conditions most of the time.

But as if that were not handicap enough, nature has imbedded the solar system in a region of great and permanent dust clouds. The total matter in the Milky Way amounts to some two hundred billion solar masses—that is, it is two hundred billion times heavier than the sun—and the sun weighs 1,000,000,000,000,000,000,000,000,000 tons. Half of the matter exists in the form of stars, a hundred billion of them. The rest is mostly gas. But a small fraction, about a billion solar masses or one half of one per cent, is interstellar dust, and this is the chief ingredient of the cosmic smog which is spread through the plane of the Milky Way and envelops the sun and the earth.

Dust hides much of the universe from us. The vast majority of the stars are blotted out of the skies by a dust fog impenetrable even to the 200-inch Palomar telescope. About two billion galaxies lie within the range of this instrument, and the fog obscures half of them.

The existence of this haze was not definitely proved until about twenty years ago. Before then astronomers were misled by their own observations, time and again. They believed that black regions and dark lanes in space, apparently empty "rifts" in the skies, were starless places. Giant clouds relatively close to the sun were mistaken for the outer edge of the Milky Way and its size was underestimated accordingly. Stars dimmed by intervening clouds were thought to be more distant than they actually are. It is no wonder that interstellar matter was regarded as a nuisance, something nature had put there to discourage our explanations.

We have been hemmed in, confined to a pitifully small region of the galaxy. Using the latest optical instruments we can see for a maximum distance of fifteen thousand light-years within the galactic disk. Really thorough investigations have extended only to approximately half that distance, or about one-fourteenth of the distance across the galaxy, which hardly gives us an impressive panorama. We are limited in many directions. Light does not reach us from the center or from the rim of the Milky Way. We might as well be sitting before a television set watching a World Series game, seeing the little group at home plate—umpire, catcher, batter—and nothing else. Much credit is due to astronomers, who on the basis of such poor viewing conditions have deduced so much about stellar events and the rules of the "game."

Now, after centuries, it is possible to find out what is happening beyond the haze. The curtain of dust has not been lifted, but we can observe through it, which is the next best thing. Radio waves from hydrogen can pass through thick clouds of dust which dim or obscure the light waves from the stars. The difference is a matter of relative sizes. Interstellar dust consists of countless particles, including a large number of ice needles and ice crystals that measure only a few millionths of an inch from one end to the other.

These invisible particles represent sizable obstacles to light rays, especially those of the shortest wave lengths which are of similar dimensions. But radio waves pass through intact, and the main reason is that they are much longer than light waves. Dust particles may be massive boulders and road blocks to light waves, but radio waves "roll" over them like a Patton tank over grains of sand or an ocean liner over the ripples produced by a rowboat. This is the basic fact upon which radio astronomers have founded a new field in their science.

## SPEEDS AND DISTANCES

It is important to emphasize the significance of listening in to broadcasts of hydrogen. If it had been practically any other element, investigators would also have been interested and would undoubtedly have obtained valuable information. But hydrogen is the predominant element of the universe. Other elements are built out of it, and its condensations produce stars and nebulae. Hydrogen is everywhere between the stars, and its signals tell us exactly where it is and in what quantities, so that we can explore hitherto inaccessible regions of space. Tracing concentrations of hydrogen is the latest technique for mapping the elusive structure of the Milky Way.

Radio astronomy is extending our galactic horizons many times. Radio telescopes like the one in Kootwijk detect signals through dust clouds just as they do through the densest fogs of the earth's atmosphere. "It gives you a queer feeling to look at the present situation when you are a little older, as I am," Oort told me in Leiden. "Things have happened so quickly. From the start of my career I have been interested in the structure of the galaxy. Then suddenly there comes a new tool which gives you in a few years a hundred times more than you could have hoped to get in a lifetime."

Using the new tool, however, calls for some delicate and subtle experimental methods. It is now possible to do far more than tune in on hydrogen broadcasts—to turn the radio dial to a particular setting, as it were, and simply note that there is hydrogen in a certain direction. There is also an exciting new way of gathering additional facts without which the radio techniques would be of considerably less value. We can not only tune in on hydrogen, we can tune in on hydrogen at different distances.

The general method may be illustrated by a hypothetical radio set with a dial designed for very fine tuning and marked off in distances. Readings of "0," "500," "1,000," "1,500," and so on, represent that many light-years, and the positions in between represent in-between distances. To investigate space at a distance of 1,300 light-years, the only thing to do is adjust the dial to the proper setting and listen to the sharp clear monotone of hydrogen atoms. At 1,500 light-years the element might come through with a higher note, while the sound of the most remote hydrogen clouds might be the equivalent of high C.

Of course, this is not how the method works in practice. Investigators do not twirl the dials of radio telescopes and tune in manually on regions located at various distances. But, in effect, the same results take place automatically. The instrument, like a good robot, makes all the dial settings and provides the usual records of inked hills and valleys on chart paper. The records furnish the measurements that must be "reduced"—that is, analyzed and interpreted in terms of astronomical findings. Translating raw data into distances, for example, depends on a detailed knowledge of how the Milky Way spins.

We live in the midst of immense stretches of stars, gas and dust, and all of it is moving and shifting and changing all the time. Imagine standing on the bridge of a ship looking ahead, out over a sea whose boundaries lie at enormous distances beyond the horizon. To all intents and purposes, it is an infinite sea. Its waters form a vast spinning vortex, a superwhirlpool which is rotating in a clockwise direction and whose center lies somewhere behind you, another infinity away. Your ship, caught up in the currents, is moving in an orbit like a tiny planet, drifting in a strong, steady, circular tide.

This sea does not rotate all together, as if it were a single piece. A closer analogy is what happens in a cup of coffee that has just been stirred vigorously. Waters spin most rapidly in the neighborhood of the center and tend to slow down more and more the closer you come to the outer boundaries. Thus ships toward the remote boundaries move at lower speeds; sooner or later your ship will catch up and then rotate past them until they are out of sight. Ships nearer the center, however, are in faster lanes and will outrace your ship.

In their surveys of interstellar hydrogen, radio astronomers are looking out over a spinning celestial sea, the plane of the Milky Way disk. Furthermore, the galaxy is also spinning like the vigorously stirred fluid in a cup. We can think of it as a system of many circular tracks, all surrounding the same center. The largest track, the one running around the outer edge of the galaxy, is 100,000 light-years in diameter and contains the slowest traffic. All the stars, nebulae and clouds in that track move together at about the same speed. Objects in the smaller track which includes the sun and our radio telescopes —diameter, 52,000 light-years—move more rapidly.

Now suppose we are observing in such a direction that a concentration of hydrogen gas lies slightly beyond us, that is, in a track larger than ours but nearby. If the gas cloud is ahead of us, we certainly gain on it because we are in a faster traffic lane. In other words, we come closer and closer to it— and this is the critical point as far as radio astronomers are concerned.

That hydrogen cloud is sending radio signals to us. Normally those signals have a wave length of about 21 centimeters, "normally" being when our receiver and the cloud are maintaining the same distance from one another. But if we are approaching the cloud, the recorded wave length is somewhat shortened. This is an example of the so-called Doppler effect. The same thing happens when you approach a train and the locomotive whistle blows. The noise you hear has a higher pitch than it would have if you had not been moving toward the whistle, which is simply another way of saying that your ear detects shortened sound waves. It is as if a steel spring were stretching from you to the source of the sound. Moving closer relaxes the spring so that the distance between the coils —the "wave length"—becomes less.

On the other hand, if you move away from the source, the spring extends and the coils are stretched further apart—the "wave length" increases. This effect may also be noted in radio astronomy. If the hydrogen cloud we are observing happens to lie in a faster lane than ours and is already ahead of us (the lane would be nearer the center of the Milky Way), it will leave us behind. Its waves will be "stretched out" as the distance increases, and our instruments will record a wave length slightly in excess of the "normal" value.

Here is how the theory works out in interpreting the sort of record obtained by the Dutch radio telescope at Kootwijk. Laboratory experiments show that when the electron of a hydrogen atom flips over, it emits a radio signal with a wave length of 21.1049 centimeters. The telescope is "listening" in a certain direction, automatically tuning in to a portion of the sky on a wide range of different wave lengths close to the laboratory value, and writing a continuous record of what is observed.

Now suppose we examine the chart later and notice two humps on it, representing two regions of concentrated hydrogen. We observe that the peak of one hump does not come at a point which represents the normal wave length of 21.1049 centimeters. Instead it is recorded at some slightly shorter wave length, say, 21.1045 centimeters. The difference is tiny, less than the thickness of a strand in a spider's web, but the receiver's circuits can detect even smaller changes. Recalling the relaxed-spring analogy, we know that a shorter wave length means we are coming closer to the observed hydrogen cloud, that we are overtaking it in our eternal merry-go-round ride about the galactic center.

The exact amount of the shortening indicates how fast we are catching up, and therefore how great a distance separates us from the cloud. With figures we used above, it turns out that the cloud is more than 2,600 light-years away from us toward the rim of the Milky Way, or nearly 30,000 light-years from the galactic center. It lies in a circular track where the average traffic speed is 126 miles a second, or more than 450,000 miles an hour. Some indication of the size of the galaxy appears in the fact that even at such rates the cloud, and everything else in the same track, takes nearly two hundred million years to make one complete circuit around the center. (The sun, being a little nearer the center, moves in a faster lane at 130 miles a second—and completes the circuit in less than 195,000,000 years).

We still have not analyzed that second hump on the chart. The hydrogen cloud it represents sends radio signals whose received wave length is somewhat longer than the normal value, 21.1054 instead of 21.1049 centimeters. This means the cloud is receding, leaving us behind. It lies closer to the galactic center, in a faster lane where the prevailing traffic speed is 135 miles a second, which represents a distance of about 23,000 light-years from the center. Deductions like these can be based on actual charts.

Such records also have a good deal to say about factors other than distances. The width and height of a hump may help indicate the dimensions of a cloud. For instance, our example shows that the cloud in the outer or slow traffic lane is about 250 light-years in diameter and more than a thousand light-years thick. Careful analysis also provides information about the speed, turbulence and mass of observed concentrations of hydrogen.

The chart we have been describing is cited as a general example only. The meaning of a particular set of humps depends, among other things, on what part of the Milky Way is being observed. Moreover, interpretations may also depend on the experience of the interpreter, and some records are as open to as many different opinions as a chart of stock-market trends. Conclusions have to be checked, rechecked and compared with evidence provided by optical telescopes.

The results of these careful studies more than justify the enthusiasm and hopes of Oort and other astronomers who feel that radio research has brought a significant breakthrough in our continuing efforts to understand the universe.

## TWISTING PATTERNS

A radio telescope tuned to hydrogen points out into space; it is a remote listening post on the speck of matter which is the earth. Along its line of sight it observes several regions of concentrated hydrogen gas, each at a different distance from the sun and from the galactic center. The regions are detected as humps on a chart. The telescope turns in a wide arc, sweeping the skies like a lighthouse beacon. It scans around in the plane of the Milky Way and moves up and down, above and below the plane.

Months of records accumulate. We are mapping our galaxy, plotting the positions of its hydrogen masses. We are learning where the gas is thickest and where thinnest, discovering the most dense regions and the bleak, almost empty regions between them. Patterns emerge gradually. We find patterns which are not entirely strange to us. The general features confirm our hunches and our theories, but the details are a revelation. As we suspected from our other research, hydrogen is heavily concentrated in the spiral arms—and in mapping hydrogen concentration we are observing them at last. At last we have built a mirror in which we can see ourselves.

Hydrogen in the galaxy, like seaweed in a tidal eddy or smoke in a spinning wind, becomes a thing of spirals. The spiral arms are turbulent streams, slender tentacles which may be more than 150,000 light-years long and form complex patterns in and near the galactic plane. They come twisting in and out of the plane, tilted at different angles with respect to one another. Our job now is to obtain a faithful image of the spiral system and then to figure out how it got that way. Finally, we may hope to predict the future of our system and of life, a process which has gained a foothold in at least one of the spirals.

The nearest spiral arm detected by its radio waves is about 12,000 light-years long—in any case, that is the extent that has been traced so far. Its outer edge is some 1,500 light-years away from us, and the arm includes the great Orion nebula. It also includes the sun, which lies near the inner edge. The observation that the earth and the whole solar system are part of a spiral arm supports previous evidence based on different observations. One argument, which was first suggested six years ago, points out that the sun is surrounded by blue supergiants and dust in the plane of the Milky Way, a situation characteristic of the spirals of Andromeda.

A recent and continuing astronomical study also locates the sun in a spiral arm. It takes advantage of the fact that very hot stars ionize or electrify nearby hydrogen so that the gas glows. Like the full moon on certain hazy nights, they may be surrounded by luminous halos up to 250 light-years in diameter. Since the hottest stars are concentrated in spiral arms, it should be possible to trace the courses of those arms by locating the halos. Taking such an approach, W. W. Morgan and his associates at the University of Chicago discovered part of the arm which includes the sun and the Orion nebula. This work has been confirmed by even more recent research on the distribution of interstellar matter and star clusters.

The Chicago investigators went further. They found a second spiral arm about 7,000 light-years from the first, out toward the rim of the Milky Way. This is called the Perseus arm because it has been associated with the great double star cluster of that constellation. A third, inner arm has also been located. It contains certain particularly bright electrified hydrogen clouds in the constellation of Sagittarius, the Archer, and lies 4,500 light-years away between the sun and the galactic center. These studies, based on difficult and precise measurements of stellar spectra and distances, are a brilliant example of the use of modern optical methods. But because of obscuring dust optical methods cannot be expected to yield information much beyond the 10,000 light-year limit.

Radio astronomy recognizes no such limits. It has not only found the three nearest spiral arms, thus providing a check of Morgan's work, but has followed them for much greater distances. The Perseus arm wraps itself around the galactic center in a great sweeping curve and has been traced from a point near the sun to the opposite side of the Milky Way. This arc and others were first charted by the Kootwijk radio telescope, which has detected hydrogen some 60,000 light-years away, a distance six times greater than conventional telescopes can penetrate into our galaxy.

At least two new, remote arms have been discovered by radio techniques. One lies nearer the galactic center than the Sagittarius arm. The other is believed to be the outermost spiral arm of our galaxy. It is about 47,000 light-years from the center, beyond the Perseus arm and close to the edge of the Milky Way disk. Judging by the patterns of other galaxies— Andromeda is known to have eleven arms—other spiral arms will almost certainly be found. And their structure will probably turn out to be extremely complex.

American as well as Dutch and Australian observers are already gathering information which hints at the devious courses of spirals in the Milky Way. The first hydrogen surveys were taken mainly to get the general lay of the land, to chart broad structures and contours. Now carefully planned regional surveys are beginning to go into the detailed anatomy of our galaxy. We know that some of the spiral arms are not simple strands but may be intricately branched. Present evidence makes out a strong case for the branching of the Orion arm, for example, the one which includes the sun.

If the evidence is confirmed, it may help explain the significance of an old astronomical finding. For more than a century astronomers have known of a peculiar concentration of matter near the sun, a kind of sheet or flattened cluster of hundreds of stars. Named Gould's Belt after one of the first investigators to describe it, the sheet is tilted at an angle to the Milky Way. Recent radio studies conducted by A. Edward Lilley and

David S. Heeschen at Harvard show that there is also a "sheet" of hydrogen which corresponds closely to the plane of the peculiar local star system and may contain as much as 100,000 solar masses of the gas. This new finding, together with previous optical observations, may be another sign of a branching of the Orion arm.

Another problem connected with the structure of our galaxy has apparently been solved. For some time it has not been definitely known whether the arms lead or trail, whether the spiral system is unwinding or winding. Now radio studies of interstellar hydrogen and optical studies of luminous hydrogen clouds agree on this point. The spiral arms trail. The central region of the Milky Way is spinning faster than the outer regions, so that it is always gaining on the arms. Our spiral galaxy is winding itself up like a tightening watchspring or spaghetti around a fork. Andromeda spins in the same way.

This discovery is especially interesting because it fits in with recent theories about the evolution of galaxies. According to some astronomers, in the beginning there is nothing but a vast irregular thing of gas clouds and stars, a system in the early stages of condensation from the cosmic background material. The embryo galaxy has no form, only a natural tendency to spin. Form comes later, with the appearance, no one knows just how or why, of the faintest traces of spirals. The next stage may be the so-called open-spiral star system in which arms appear as more definite structures but the nucleus or center is relatively small and unshaped.

Then, as the galaxy winds up, the arms wrap tighter and tighter around the nucleus, which becomes larger and larger. They are short-lived, because a galactic rotation or two is more than enough to rip these ribbons to shreds. A rotation or two may take a few hundred million years, and spirals cannot last that long. Spirals of the Milky Way may endure fifty million years, which is only a small part of the galaxy's estimated life span of some ten billion years. For all their spiral glory the arms fade as swiftly as cloud patterns at sunset. Translated into human terms, they occupy between six months and a year of an average life span.

A galaxy in its final stages has no spiral arms, and since it is old and may have collided with other galaxies, it has probably been swept clean of almost all its gas and dust. That means it is sterile, having lost its ability to beget new stars, which must come from interstellar matter. It consists almost entirely of a huge and well-formed nucleus which may be egg-shaped or spherical. What started as an irregular mass, a cosmic cloud of jagged outlines, ends in its senility with a rounded, symmetrical shape. So stones jostled in the bed of a stream are worn smooth as time and water pass.

This is one version of the life history of an average galaxy. So far we have considered the fleeting spiral arms only, and ignored the enduring center. But hydrogen studies may also tell us about the heart of the Milky Way, which is hidden by layers of interstellar matter so dense that it could not be observed directly until a decade or so ago, when Reber first saw it by radio light.

Radio telescopes receiving hydrogen signals from the center of our galaxy show what optical studies have previously indicated, that the center consists of a large core of concentrated gases and extra-intense radio broadcasts. It has been estimated to contain at least a hundred million solar masses of material. These central regions have no spiral structure, or at least the tangle is so great that we have not yet distinguished any pattern. They are known to contain a large number of what one astronomer has called "stellar jaywalkers," stars that do not remain in the circular traffic lanes of the Milky Way but move at all angles across the lanes.

Direct studies of the matter at the galactic center are just beginning. Many investigators believe that they may turn out to be even more significant than studies of the outer spiral arms. Perhaps the secret of the growth of galaxies is locked at the center of things, just as the secret of life itself seems to be locked in the nucleus of the cell. In the case of star systems as well as living things the basic problem is how symmetry develops out of chaos. How and why do galaxies evolve from irregular masses to spirals, and then to "solid" globes or elliptical bodies?

We know something about the spiral patterns of the earth. We know that a whirlpool may be the result of disturbances

Out of changing, flowing stuff a more enduring thing arises . . .
there are stars where before there was only swirling matter . . .
The new star is a blazing hot body, a sizzling core in a great and
cool mass of gas and dust. There is an explosion of enormous proportions (A). Gases near the star expand rapidly. A ballooning shell
of hot gases is produced whose front forms powerful shock waves.
When the blast strikes cooler gases more remote from the hot star
at the core, they are compressed by the sledge-hammer impact (B),
and secondary hot stars, offspring of the original star, may condense along the front of the shock wave (C). Other stars may come
by a kind of chain reaction.

*The Great Nebula in Orion . . . a breeding place of stars.*

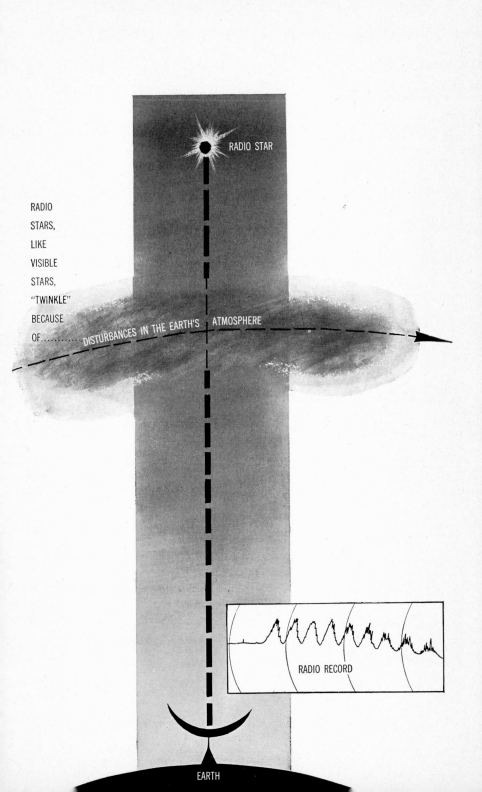

RADIO STAR

RADIO
STARS,
LIKE
VISIBLE
STARS,
"TWINKLE"
BECAUSE
OF........... DISTURBANCES IN THE EARTH'S ATMOSPHERE

RADIO RECORD

EARTH

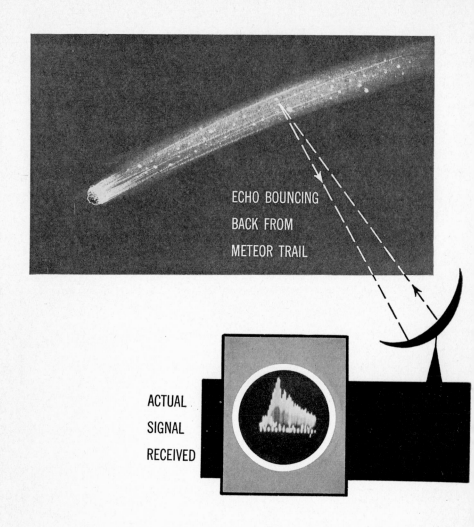

ECHO BOUNCING
BACK FROM
METEOR TRAIL

ACTUAL
SIGNAL
RECEIVED

*Detecting meteors by radar astronomy.*

arising deep beneath the surface, waters pouring down a hole or sucked around in a vortex. And we know that cyclones mark the coming together of air masses from the tropics and from subzero polar regions, air masses twisted, by the earth's spinning, into whirlpools of wind. But we do not know what spinning masses and forces are involved in the shaping of galaxies. Galaxies, whirlpools of gas and stars, come and go according to laws as yet undiscovered. This is the mystery of mysteries which astronomers, armed with new radio techniques, hope ultimately to penetrate.

# 12

## INSIDE THE SPIRAL ARMS

Birth and aging and death are to be found throughout the universe. We have discussed one theory about the life cycle of a galaxy, which may pass from shapeless infancy to a late elliptical structure, with a strange and beautiful spiral interlude somewhere before middle age. But great and striking changes in the galaxy are themselves an organic expression of many lesser changes, the collective life cycles of many individual stars. In an analogous manner, our bodies as they develop express changes among billions of individual cells.

Spiral arms are among the places in space where things are being born and are dying. Within the arms, local knots or concentrations of interstellar matter produce stars just as concentrations of intergalactic matter may produce Milky Ways. And when we consider things on a smaller, local scale, we are getting closer to home. The more we learn about the creation of stars, the better we shall understand the origin of the earth and the entire solar system. This remote beginning is the first stage in a process that has organized matter from a diluted haze in space to a thing of infinitely varied forms—of which life is the latest, perhaps the most complex but certainly not the last.

All we have to go on is recently obtained records of past events. Our photographs furnish images of stars as they appeared many hundreds of thousands of years ago, when the light we record today started on its journey through space. The images are light which has been trapped and preserved, fixed like a fossil insect in a piece of amber. Like fossils, they are remnants of other times, pictures of things that exist no more. The intricate patterns of stellar evolution can be revealed only by studying and comparing record after record, image after image. Now with the discovery of radio images we are increasing our knowledge, particularly of the earliest processes that account for the birth of stars.

The natural processes which may be called creation are not completed, a fact that astronomers have come to realize only during the past generation or so. Whatever her objectives, nature has not finished evolution in either the biological or the physical sense. Right now uncounted births are taking place in the Milky Way and in hundreds of millions of other galaxies. New stars—and probably new planets and new moons as well—are hatching in the nearest stellar breeding site, the Orion nebula, among other places. Imbedded in thick clouds like eggs in a nest, they are so warm that they could not have been there long.

These stars, blazing with the heat of nuclear furnaces, mark the exact spots of recent creation. They are under close and continuous scrutiny at all observatories and by all available techniques. No aspect of astronomical research depends more on the joint efforts of radio and optical investigators. Electronic scanning with radio telescopes is providing new information, but as often as not it would be impossible to interpret the information without drawing heavily on the results of traditional stargazing.

We want, above all, to understand the mechanisms of physical creation. It is not enough to say that stars condense out of interstellar matter. We want to know how the process works, what forces cause diffuse gases to form stars and gleaming clusters of stars.

## GAS AND DUST

The Harvard College Observatory has its main group of telescopes, including a 60-inch instrument, about forty miles from Boston. The George R. Agassiz Station has been built on top of a hill known as Oak Ridge, a name more famous as that of the town in Tennessee where one of the nation's largest atomic-energy factories is. Work going on at "the other Oak Ridge" in Massachusetts, however, may have results at least as spectacular. Bart Bok and his associates have launched a broad and expanding program in radio astronomy, the largest of its kind at any American university. Much of the information in this section depends on the work accomplished in this program by John Campbell, Frank Drake, May Kassim, R. S. Lawrence, Thomas Matthews, T. K. Menon and Campbell Wade—as well as Bok, Ewen, Heeschen and Lilley.

The program involves new observations of 21-centimeter radio waves, including further studies of spiral arms in the Milky Way. But Harvard astronomers are also looking at special regions within the spiral arms, the great nebulae or clouds where stars are being formed. Among their instruments is a radio telescope with a 25-foot aerial that looks like the searchlight model the Dutch use at Kootwijk. Designed by Harold Ewen, it was hauled by truck along the narrow dirt road that winds up the side of Oak Ridge, a feat which rates as a minor engineering triumph.

One hydrogen survey has covered a huge complex of nebulae stretching across the constellations of Perseus, Taurus and Orion. As the telescope scanned the skies, sweeping back and forth across the boundaries of the nebulae, the record showed a sharp increase in the intensity of radio signals emitted by hydrogen particles. This meant an increase in the concentration of the gas. It is estimated that this entire system of nebulae contains some twenty thousand solar masses of hydrogen, so distributed that every cubic inch contains 125 hydrogen atoms—which is about seven times more dense than an average interstellar region in the plane of the Milky Way.

Inside such nebulae are certain regions where obscuring material is unusually thick. The regions show up in sharp and jagged outline against a brilliant background of celestial footlights, glowing gases and bright, hot stars. Some of them appear as smokelike wisps. Others are spherical masses that Bok has called globules. They may measure from a fifth of a light-year to nearly two light-years across—from a thousand billion to twelve thousand billion miles—and have an average mass equivalent to two or three suns. The largest globule is the Coal Sack, a great dark blob which can be seen in the southern skies and contains 650 solar masses of material.

These are the darkest and densest stretches of interstellar space, black "storm clouds" which produce no lightning or thunder that we can detect and have endured for ages. Since they are stellar breeding places, it was reasonable to suspect that they contained more hydrogen than other parts of the nebulae in which they lie. The notion was particularly plausible because of hydrogen's place as the most common element in the universe. But radio observations point toward an entirely different conclusion. Judging by the intensity of hydrogen broadcasts, the gas is no more concentrated in globules than it is in much thinner parts of the same nebula.

Presumably the extra-concentrated material is dust, and more than a year ago Bok set out to obtain fresh evidence to support the point. He visited the Mount Wilson and Mount Palomar observatories for a "star-counting spree" that lasted two weeks. He selected special photographic negatives covering wide regions of the skies, placed them on a glass plate illuminated from behind and examined them through a binocular microscope. He was making a detailed count of the stars in a great nebula in the constellation of Ophiuchus, the Serpent Holder, which lies toward the center of the Milky Way.

The study covered about eight square degrees of sky. At the distance of the nebula, such an area can be represented as a square each side of which is 18.5 light-years long. Bok divided the area into a checkerboard or crossword-puzzle pattern consisting of more than a thousand smaller squares, each about half a light-year—3,000,000,000,000 miles—on each side. Then he painstakingly counted every visible star in each box, a standard procedure in astronomy. The idea is to estimate the quantity of interstellar dust in different areas indirectly, by estimating its obscuring effects. This procedure depends on the assumption, which checks well with available evidence, that within the plane of the Milky Way stars are distributed uniformly in neighboring celestial regions. In other words, nearby regions in the same area should contain about the same number of stars.

If actual star counts reveal marked differences in distribution, interstellar dust can probably be blamed. Careful counts within a given nebula may show that fifty to a hundred stars are visible in one region, while another box in the same area of the same nebula may contain only half a dozen stars or none at all. Presumably the regions showing the fewest stars are the dustiest. The difference provides a rough measure of the amount of light-scattering material between our telescopes and the objects we attempt to study. In his box-by-box survey of the Ophiuchus nebula, Bok counted between 25,000 and 30,000 individual stars.

This work revealed that dust, but not hydrogen, is unusually thick in the blackest regions of the nebula. In fact, it gets thicker from the outside in, and an appreciable proportion of the densest spots lie toward the center. Dust is not distributed evenly through nebulae. It may be ten to fifteen times more concentrated in some regions than in others, and these are the extra-dusty places where creation seems to be proceeding most rapidly.

## THE BIRTH OF STARS

Radio and optical astronomy have combined to give us a more precise understanding than ever before of the main ingredients which go into the making of new stars. And the facts check with a theory of how the process works. Imagine a region in which a nebula happens to have come into being, or rather, a slight concentration of gas which is hardly dense enough yet to rate as a full-fledged nebula. Some of the atoms in the gas collide and stick to one another. Groups of atoms and molecules combine into somewhat larger particles, clusters of matter like grapes in a bunch.

Of course, it may take a long time for the particles to come together. So little matter is to be found in interstellar space that a lone atom may wander about for eons and eons before it encounters another atom. But there are so many atoms and so much time that encounters must and do take place. Time is nature's most impressive and important asset in her ceaseless experiments. Given a supply of matter and sufficient time, it seems that anything is possible.

Sooner or later dust particles will form in the gas. These motes can be regarded as nuclei, atomic recruiting places, centers where matter is built into more complex forms. They are much larger than atoms, larger than a cliff compared with a grain of sand. They contain water frozen into ice crystals and other hydrogen compounds such as ammonia and methane, or marsh gas. Iron, nickel and other metals included in the list of stellar ingredients are also locked inside dust particles. Incidentally, only a small fraction of gaseous material turns into dust. The hydrogen in an average nebula weighs about a hundred times more than the dust particles, and for every single particle there are about a thousand billion hydrogen atoms.

How are the rare dust particles concentrated in star-forming globules? According to one theory, starlight plays a major role in the process. Light waves are streams of energy, like air jets or water spurting out of the nozzle of a hose. They exert a definite force on everything they strike. Sunny parts of the roof of a house, for example, actually "sag" a bit compared with parts in the shade because they are exposed to the extra burden of solar radiation. The pressure is exceedingly delicate, many times more delicate than that of an ant's foot on concrete. But acting on tiny dust particles over long periods of time, it can produce significant changes.

A light ray traveling through interstellar space strikes a dust particle, pushing it in a given direction. Particles behind the one that is pushed receive little or no impact, and the light does not seriously disturb their peace, but the struck particle is driven nearer to its protected neighbors. As centuries tick off, this effect tends to drive dust particles closer and closer together. The pressure of light produces increasingly crowded conditions, and after the crowding passes a certain point, things somehow become ripe for the final stages. Just as flow-ing water may freeze solid under the right conditions, so celes-tial bodies may be created in a milieu of gas and dust. Out of changing, flowing stuff a more enduring thing arises. There is a star, and perhaps a number of planets-to-be, where before there has been only swirling matter.

We do not know exactly how such a star is formed. Star-light is relatively slow-acting and gentle, and something more may be needed to stimulate creation, perhaps gravitational forces that cause matter to contract into a smaller volume. But the original star is a trigger or fuse. Once it has been formed in a nebula, other stars may come by a kind of chain reaction. The new star is a blazing hot body full of energy, a sizzling core in a great cool mass of gas and dust, and it comes into being "suddenly," which in astronomical terms means within a period of a hundred thousand years.

The result is an explosion of enormous proportions. Gases near the star are raised to temperatures of twenty thousand de-grees Fahrenheit or more, and expand rapidly. A ballooning shell of hot gases is produced whose front forms powerful shock waves like the house-leveling blasts of a bomb. When the blast strikes cooler gases, they are compressed by the sledgehammer impact, and secondary stars, offspring of the original hot star, may condense along the front of the shock wave.

This theory is suggested in a recent study by Jan Oort and Lyman Spitzer. It is based largely on research concerning hy-drogen clouds drifting in the spiral arms of the Milky Way. Twenty-one-centimeter radio waves provide direct evidence of the motion, as well as the presence, of interstellar hydrogen. Properly interpreted, properly decoded, the waves become com-plicated and highly technical messages from nature. We can learn a great deal by reading them, although the language may be strange and some of the subtlest points may elude us. Ide-ally, the signal from a hydrogen cloud would appear on the charts as a steep "spike," a high and narrow peak which repre-sents the ultimate in clear sharp tuning. It is the radio equiva-lent of a photograph in perfect focus, in which every detail of the image stands out sharply.

This kind of signal would be obtained if the hydrogen cloud, like the sun, were circling smoothly in its course around the galactic center. Then it would be moving regularly and parallel to us, and its radio image would be a clear one. But actually the image is blurred. There are practically no spike markings on the charts. In most directions the signal appears as a relatively broad hump, a spread-out, "smeared" sort of record coming from a large concentration of clouds. Not only that, but the record may show signs of approaching or receding motions which have nothing to do with velocities in faster or slower traffic lanes.

Ordinarily blurring is a nuisance. If cameras produced comparably fuzzy pictures, photographs would hardly be worth taking. But part of the art of research is to put the difficulties to work, to make a positive advantage out of the most stubborn obstacles if they cannot be eliminated or circumvented. After all, the entire science of radio astronomy grew out of an effort to overcome an obstacle, to understand the bothersome effects of static on transatlantic communications. Similarly, the blurring of 21-centimeter signals has turned out to be a source of valuable information.

The trouble is that hydrogen clouds will not sit still and pose for us. They will not even move regularly so that we can at least predict, and allow for, their paths through the skies. But we have a way of measuring their restlessness in the fuzziness of radio records. The faster an individual cloud moves in its random course, the more blurred its radio image—that is, the broader the inked hump it makes on the chart.

Our records show wide variations in the speeds of hydrogen clouds. The "Sunday drivers" are ambling along at little more than a thousand miles an hour, while speeders may travel a hundred times faster. The average speed of the clouds seems to be about twenty thousand miles an hour. These puffs of galactic gas swirl and twist as they move about, and they are extremely turbulent inside. Astronomers report similar findings with ordinary telescopes in studies of light from distant stars. Characteristic dark lines in the spectra of the stars indicate the presence and motion of intervening clouds. Thus radio and light waves tell the same story. Hydrogen clouds are celestial hurricanes, highly turbulent masses which sweep in unpredictable paths through the Milky Way.

The speed and turbulence of the clouds are extremely important in star formation, which requires high temperatures and pressures and vigorous mixing. No new stars would appear if hydrogen clouds slowed down. And yet this is exactly what might be expected. There are enough clouds so that they collide once every ten million years, or at least several hundred times since the formation of the galaxy. Such frequent collisions mean that, if it were not for other forces, the clouds would lose energy like caroming billiard balls and ultimately roll to a stop. The forces that counteract the slowing-down tendency may be traced to the heat of newborn stars.

This is a life-giving heat in the most basic sense. Because of it gases expand, stars and planets form, and life gains footholds on local condensations scattered among the clouds and nebulae in the spiral arms of galaxies. It works in a great cycle. A new star stirs up gases, which lead to the formation of more new stars, which stir up more gases forming more stars, and so on and on. Creation, once it starts and wherever and however it starts, is a self-continuing process.

## ABSORBED WAVES

There is another radio method of studying the matter between stars, a method which has been used for only about two years. Radio waves coming directly from concentrations of hydrogen are like messages delivered intact from station to station. They reach our receivers at full strength and leave the familiar markings on our charts, inked humps and peaks representing increases in signal intensity. But expected messages that do not reach us may also provide important information. If a ten-year-old boy let loose in a roomful of toys makes no noise, we have every reason to suspect that something unusual is going on. Similarly, radio astronomers have found that certain "silences" which occur during the scanning of radio skies have special significance.

The new research involves precise studies of signals from the most intense objects in the radio sky, radio stars. A radio star broadcasts powerfully, and in a buckshot fashion. If you had a radio set of the right type, you would tune in on the star wherever you turned the dial. It pours out waves of all lengths and throughout the entire radio range. But we do not receive all the waves at full strength. The 21-centimeter signals, for example, may be somewhat weakened because they must first pass through interstellar hydrogen—and hydrogen not only emits such waves on its own, but also absorbs them when they come from other sources. The gas acts somewhat like a thick curtain which muffles sounds from the next room.

One summer night in 1954 two young Naval Research Laboratory investigators were looking for this effect. Edward Lilley, who had transferred from Harvard, and Edward McLain were using the laboratory's aluminum radio telescope to scan the skies in the region of the Cassiopeia source, the most intense radio star known. They expected that 21-centimeter waves from Cass would come in at a reduced intensity because of the absorbing action of interstellar hydrogen. Suddenly McLain pointed to the chart: "Look, we've got a hole in the record—a big one!"

The "hole" was a strange marking on the chart. What had been expected was a hump, a somewhat lower hump indicating weaker 21-centimeter signals. Instead the recording pen had swung down to make a sharp dip or depression. At first the equipment was suspected. Perhaps the electronic circuits had been acting up again. But three weeks of checking showed that the radio telescope was working beautifully. The dips were real effects. Something out of the ordinary was taking place in space.

Lilley figured out the theoretical aspects of the answer. Signals from Cass were not passing through a thin haze of hydrogen, but through relatively heavy concentrations which are dense enough to absorb or muffle a high proportion of 21-centimeter radio waves. It turns out that the gas is probably concentrated in individual clouds about eighteen light-years in diameter. Careful analyses of the records are also telling us about the distribution of the clouds. For example, one type of record includes three distinct dips which are believed to represent three distinct clouds.

Furthermore, the clouds are located in spiral arms—and that fact serves as the basis of a suggested radio method of gauging the distances of radio stars in the Milky Way. According to Lilley and McLain, one of the clouds lies in a near arm, while the other two lie in an arm about 10,000 light-years from the earth. Since the signals from Cass pass through clouds in both arms, the radio star is at least that far away.

If this research stands up, we shall have to revise our distance estimates for the Cassiopeia radio star and perhaps for other objects as well. But the matter is still far from settled. Palomar observers have new optical evidence which indicates that the source may be less than fifteen hundred, not ten thousand, light-years away. In radio studies that depend on the absorption of hydrogen signals we are observing single clouds rather than great cloud complexes. It is more difficult to deduce the distances of individual clouds than of groups, and that fact may influence the interpretation of results. The verdict at present: no decision.

Rodney Davies and David Williams at Jodrell Bank have announced an interesting study of absorbed hydrogen signals coming from another direction. Observing toward the center of the Milky Way, they have found an intense radio source at a reported distance of about 9,800 light-years. In other words, an extremely strong transmitter seems to be lying nearly in our line of sight to the galactic center. McLain, taking advantage of the exceptional focusing power of the navy's huge aluminum aerial, has also obtained detailed records of this source and places it at about the same distance.

After their discovery, the English investigators started looking through astronomical atlases and papers to identify the radio source, and they found a likely clue in an issue of the *Astrophysical Journal*. A report from the Yerkes and McDonald observatories, confirming and extending research by Mexican astronomers, describes a possible explanation for the radio observations. The signals may be coming from a group of thirty-eight giant blue stars, which appear as very faint objects because they are obscured by thick interstellar clouds.

The studies open up new prospects. Blue-giant stars are usually associated with great nebulae. If there is such a nebula in the direction of the center, it is hidden by clouds and ordinary telescopes cannot see it. Radio telescopes may help us find hidden nebulae, new sites of stellar evolution.

Meanwhile, Graham Smith at Cambridge has also been observing hydrogen signals, not absorbed signals but signals emitted by objects lying toward the galactic center. He also reports an intense radio source in about the same direction as the clump of blue-giant stars. But he believes it is some 26,000 light-years away. Currently there is a question as to whether Smith is observing the same source as the Jodrell Bank workers—which would indicate another controversy involving distances—or a different source located right at the galactic center itself. But one thing is certain. Hydrogen research will lead to new findings about the innermost regions of the Milky Way.

Already we know that unusual and unexplained disturbances are taking place in these regions. They include highly turbulent gases and the fastest-moving hydrogen masses known, whose top speeds may be more than 200,000 miles an hour. According to our present model, most of the matter in the galaxy moves along circular paths or traffic lanes around a relatively compact core. But increasing evidence shows that the Milky Way is not so orderly, at least not in its central zones. Here enormous concentrations of hydrogen, concentrations comparable to the quantities of matter in a great spiral arm, may be racing across circular traffic lanes. The movement toward the center may represent a major event in the tempestuous history of the galactic core. The spiral arms may be more twisted and coiled than we previously believed.

More speculative notions have also been discussed. Two of the nearest spiral arms, the Orion and Sagittarius formations, may actually be part of a single superarm which spirals directly into the nucleus. Another suggestion is that matter is streaming through the spiral arms like mighty rivers into a vast ocean basin. Some of these possibilities agree with certain theoretical ideas reported at a recent Princeton meeting of the American Astronomical Society by Frank Edmondson of Indiana University.

It is still too early to form definite conclusions, and our

current theories will certainly be modified in the light of new findings. Hydrogen research, on emitted as well as absorbed 21-centimeter waves, is attracting the interest of more and more astronomers. It offers one of the most promising techniques yet developed for observing the dense and restless zones at the heart of our galaxy.

## RESEARCH FRONTIERS

The study of 21-centimeter signals is only about five years old, and the instruments already used so extensively can be compared with Galileo's first telescopes, which yielded new and wonderful discoveries but hardly hinted at the richness of the universe. Our radio receivers have also yielded new discoveries and invaluable clues to the nature of things. But they have been blunt tools. We need greater resolution or focusing power to probe the details of galactic structure, and greater sensitivity to pick up signals we are missing now. We need radio telescopes as superior to our first efforts as present-day radio sets are to the crystal receivers of the 1920's.

Such instruments are coming. Harvard's original radio telescope on Oak Ridge already has a larger companion, officially launched in a ceremony held in April, 1956. Made possible mainly by a $132,000 grant from the National Science Foundation, it has a 60-foot antenna—a size which is readily available because such antennas are being made in large quantities for the nation's radar-defense stations in Alaska and elsewhere. As usual, Ewen designed the electronic equipment, although his colleagues had some doubts whether he would stay alive long enough to complete the job. He is still a racing-car enthusiast, and drives his Thunderbird at near-astronomical speeds.

In Washington the Carnegie Institution's Department of Terrestrial Magnetism is completing a great 84-foot instrument, built so that it can be made larger as research progresses. Another giant radio telescope, constructed specifically for hydrogen studies and related work, is already being used at the Leiden Observatory. Set up at the observatory's new Dwingelo station, it has an 82-foot parabolic antenna which weighs about forty thousand pounds. Near this giant are a pair of smaller dish-shaped antennas, "two little satellites" which were built as wartime radar aerials by the Nazis and have since been salvaged from islands off the Norwegian coast. New equipment is also being built at other radio-astronomy stations, and still larger and more elaborate devices are in the blueprint stage.

These instruments will be used in many new studies. Radio astronomers have been thinking about methods of receiving signals emitted by substances which have not yet been detected by radio methods. Since different atoms and molecules broadcast at different natural wave lengths, it should be possible to tune in on each of them separately, as if they were so many radio or television stations. Ideally, you could select your interstellar material and construct a receiver to pick up its broadcasts. The big problem is that the broadcasts may be too faint, even for supersensitive receivers.

For example, deuterium is a form of hydrogen or isotope which weighs twice as much as the common type and broadcasts at a wave length of 92 centimeters, about three feet. It may be important as a nuclear fuel during the early stages of star formation. It is also of special interest for another reason. Common hydrogen makes up such a large proportion of interstellar gas that a great deal may lie along a given line of sight. It cannot be seen through beyond a certain distance. The effect is like looking into a blazing furnace. All you see is the glare in front of you, and the radiation behind does not register. Deuterium, on the other hand, is exceedingly scarce. That means the isotope is more thinly distributed and should be picked up at greater distances.

The very scarcity of deuterium has made it difficult to detect until recently, but late in the summer of 1955, Soviet investigators announced that they had accomplished the feat. According to their report, radio waves from heavy hydrogen atoms have been obtained from the direction of the galactic center. These signals, appearing as small dips on inked records, represent absorbed radiations, and their intensity indicates that deuterium may be ten to fifteen times more concentrated toward the center of the Milky Way than it is on earth. Although the validity and implications of this work remain to be explored, it created considerable excitement when it was first revealed at a meeting of radio astronomers in England.

It may also be possible to detect another material which consists of a hydrogen atom and an oxygen atom joined in a firm bond. The signals of this substance are emitted at 17 centimeters, a wave length close to that of ordinary hydrogen.

Meanwhile, 21-centimeter studies of ordinary hydrogen continue to expand. Radio astronomers are starting to explore the distribution of the gas in Andromeda and other galaxies beyond the Milky Way. Australian investigators have made a preliminary survey of the Magellanic Clouds, the Small Cloud and the Large Cloud, a pair of irregularly shaped galaxies about 175,000 light-years away. Early voyagers in the southern seas wondered about them and called them "white clouds." Today we have identified them as the closest known star systems (Andromeda is the closest *spiral* system). These galaxies seem to be moving around the Milky Way like two planets or comets around the sun.

Radio records show that hydrogen is abundant in both clouds, a finding contrary to the previous beliefs of most astronomers. The Large Cloud is also known to contain far more dust than the Small Cloud, which may imply particularly favorable conditions for the creation of new stars. In any case, the Large Cloud seems to be in an early stage of evolution from its irregular shape to a more familiar and symmetrical form. Close inspection reveals the faintest trace of spiral arms, and the galaxy has been called an "incipient spiral." Apparently it exerts a strong gravitational pull on the Small Cloud, which has a great wing or bulge of hydrogen extending from the side nearest its more massive companion. The wing has been traced by its radio signals.

So far 21-centimeter radio astronomy has been confined to hydrogen within galaxies, interstellar hydrogen. But there is matter between the galaxies, too. Cosmic gases, the ultimate raw materials contained in star systems, go into the building of new galaxies or are hurled into space by galaxies as they spin and collide. New optical telescopes have made possible the study of intergalactic matter, and we are just beginning to observe many of its strange designs and structures.

Galaxies are not always neatly self-contained systems isolated in outer space. Some of them are parts of even vaster and more intricate patterns. Two arms of the great Whirlpool spiral galaxy, "feelers" thousands of light-years long, reach out to make contact with a neighboring irregular galaxy. Other galaxies have stretched-out arms in the form of haloes and even double haloes. Still others are connected by glowing filaments which Fritz Zwicky of the California Institute of Technology has called intergalactic bridges. These bridges span inconceivably large distances, appear as dark streaks on photographs and may be extended sheets of matter viewed edge-on.

Such phenomena are signs of important activity in the frigid regions separating galaxies. Radio techniques may help us to interpret these signs and discover new signs by furnishing the first direct evidence of hydrogen gas between star systems. This is definitely a project for the future, because the gas is so thin that new instruments will be needed to detect it. But investigators are planning their attack on the problem.

The chances of tuning in on a variety of interstellar materials are far brighter than they were in the earlier days of radio astronomy. The new science may eventually help us to study the basic stuff of the universe, cosmic gases that play a leading role in the evolution of galaxies and of the mysterious worlds inside them.

# 13

## RADAR ASTRONOMY

Most research in radio astronomy is based on the reception of radio waves coming from beyond the earth. Our radio telescopes are essentially listening devices to pick up signals generated in remote regions of the solar system and the Milky Way and other galaxies. We have nothing to do with the creation of the signals. They are produced by natural transmitters in outer space.

There is a branch of radio astronomy, however, in which the original radio waves are generated by man-made transmitters. The instruments include special aerials, often the familiar bowl-shaped type, which emit short, intense bursts of radio energy. The bursts make a round trip. They travel out through the earth's atmosphere, strike obstacles in their path, and are reflected so that they bounce back to the aerials from which they originally came. This is the principle of radar, and the research is known as radar astronomy.

Radar astronomy has its limitations. Its range is much smaller than that of radio astronomy, because we cannot hope to make transmitters as powerful as those of even relatively feeble radio stars. The power of a transmitter's signals falls off sharply as they travel further and further through space. For example, signals at ten miles are only one-hundredth as strong as signals picked up a mile away. At a hundred miles they drop to about one ten-thousandth of their one-mile value. There is also a double loss in radar astronomy. Reflected waves, radio echoes, grow weaker and weaker during every mile of the return trip. Using radar techniques we shall probably not be able to probe regions beyond the solar system. Certainly we shall never bounce signals off the stars.

But many possibilities exist within a smaller range. Radio echoes are being received routinely from the earth's atmosphere and from the moon, and plans are already being drawn up for experiments that may extend our range to the sun and some of the planets. Such research plays an important part in surveys of the upper atmosphere, where it is being used together with rocket studies and other methods. It furnishes facts about high-altitude weather conditions and about the origins of the magnetic storms that interfere with radio communications. On the astronomical side, it has practically settled one problem that has caused controversy among astronomers, and it offers a fresh attack on many unresolved problems.

## METEOR ECHOES

It is fortunate that the earth has an atmosphere. Even if we found some way of getting about in the absence of air, the surface would be pelted with far more missiles than it is now. Only about half a dozen of the objects from space reach us on an average day, and most of them are smaller than a pinhead. The rest burn up miles above the surface. These are meteors and their number is legion. It is conservatively estimated that every day eight thousand billion pieces of stone and iron enter the earth's atmosphere.

A major problem in astronomy is to discover where all this matter comes from. The problem is still unsolved, but within the past few years radar astronomy has helped bring us closer to an answer.

Until recently certain prominent astronomers believed that at least sixty per cent of all sporadic meteors—that is, the sort of "shooting star" seen during an average night—come from interstellar space. The chief evidence for this belief had been obtained by Ernst Öpik, a Lithuanian investigator now at the Armagh Observatory in Northern Ireland. He used a special rocking mirror to determine how fast meteors were traveling, and he found that most of them were moving more than 45 miles a second, and many had velocities as high as 60 to 120 miles a second. Calculations show that meteors moving at these speeds would fly out of the solar system like rocks from a slingshot. In other words, they could not be permanent members of the solar system, and must be visitors from outer space.

But, to quote a recent meteor study, Opik's observed speeds "remain an enigma." A large number of new electronic observations fail to confirm his findings, and support a position indicated many years ago in photographic studies conducted by Fred Whipple, of Harvard.

The possibility of detecting meteors by radar was suggested by work performed more than fifteen years ago. Unexpected echoes were recorded at Harvard, while in India peculiar whistles of falling pitch were heard on short-wave radio sets. Investigators at both places correctly decided that meteors were responsible for the effects. Then Stanley Hey, who demonstrated that radio waves were coming from the sun and other regions in the Milky Way used modern radar late in the war to obtain meteor echoes. Present-day radar research stems from his work. Today we observe meteors in the daytime as well as at night, and observe smaller bodies than can be detected by optical techniques.

One method, for example, uses a radar transmitter to send 150 pulses of radio energy a second into space (each pulse lasts a fifty-thousandth of a second). The pulses travel at the speed of light and bounce back, but not from meteors. Meteors are not observed directly with either radio or optical instruments. What we see in the night sky is not the shooting star itself; the chunk of matter is usually too small for that. We see the path of luminous gases where the meteor has been, like the line of white smoke behind a jet plane.

Similarly, radar sets see meteor trails. As a meteor whizzes through the atmosphere, it does an enormous amount of damage. It knocks electrons off atoms in its way, about thirty thousand billion electrons for every foot it travels, and it may travel more than ten miles. On the average, we can obtain echoes from about two miles of this wake in space before it fades away. Each echo from the wake appears as a pair of green dots or a "pip" on the radar screen.

Radar sets may be designed to transmit steady flows of radio energy instead of pulses. But in either case we obtain our information from echoes, and all techniques tell the same story as far as meteor speeds are concerned. In one fifteen-month study Donald McKinley, of the National Research Council of Canada, received echoes from nearly eleven thousand meteors. Almost all of his results were obtained from meteor trails forty-eight to seventy-two miles above the surface of the earth.

The results tend to demolish the theory that meteors arrive from beyond the solar systems. Although his instruments could measure speeds as high as ninety miles a second, McKinley found that at the most one out of every three hundred bodies moves fast enough to put it in the class of possible interstellar visitors. In fact, his conclusion is even stronger than that: "Of the thousands of meteor velocities in our records, we have not yet found one which we can definitely assert to be a meteor from interstellar space." The same general conclusion comes from studies at other meteor research centers, including Stanford University, the National Bureau of Standards and. the Jodrell Bank Experimental Station.

The vast majority of sporadic meteors must have originated in the solar system. But we do not know for certain how they were formed. They may once have been part of asteroids or minor planets, thousands of which are known to be revolving about the sun. These bodies tend to be irregularly shaped, as if they were fragments of other larger bodies. Many astronomers believe that the sun once had one or two planets which disintegrated in a colossal explosion or collision, and that asteroids are the scattered remains. Or asteroids may be pieces of a planet that never formed, chunks that never fused into a major member of the solar system, or leftover material that was not used for planet-making. In any case, many meteors may be chips broken off from bumping asteroids.

So far we have been discussing sporadic meteors only, shooting stars which appear and vanish in a random sort of way. There are also shower meteors, coming and going at definite intervals and apparently revolving as groups in elliptical orbits about the sun. The value of radar in observing showers was vividly demonstrated in 1946, when bad weather over New England ruined the plans of observers with cameras but a "radio whistle trap" at Harvard obtained echoes through the clouds and detected more than four thousand meteors. Radar investigators were also listening in at Russian and British stations.

Some relationship seems to exist between shower meteors and the six hundred-odd known comets, glowing bodies with tails which move in orbits about the sun. More than a century ago a previously observed comet made a scheduled reappearance in an unexpected form—as twin comets. It had split in two somewhere along its circuit. The double comet appeared again six years later, for the last time. But twenty years after that there was a shower of meteors as the earth passed through the orbit of the missing twins.

This strange case history inspired the notion that such meteors are debris from comets which pass too close to the sun or a large planet and are torn to bits by gravitational forces. The notion is not in good standing today. One objection is that comets tend to break into smaller comets rather than meteors. But we still suspect that comets and shower meteors have something to do with one another, although the connection is not an obvious one. Perhaps showers are simply parts of comets that have come adrift or been pulled away, dust shaken from hazy comet tails.

There are many reasons why we need to know how meteors were formed. For one thing, the knowledge would give us a far better idea of the formation of the planets and the solar system, and a good idea of how planets and solar systems are formed throughout the universe. The secret of meteor origin is to be found in a large-scale and detailed analysis of their orbits, and such work is proceeding at an accelerated pace in optical as well as radio observatories.

The detection of meteor echoes may be amazingly precise.

Modern instruments can pick up radar signals from the trails of pinhead-sized meteors whose weights have been measured in millionths of an ounce. The positions of these specks of matter can be measured to an accuracy of fifty yards or so at a distance of about six hundred miles, or better than one part in twenty thousand. Furthermore, the accuracy could be improved appreciably if it were necessary. The very speed at which the measurements are made, however, raises a problem that is becoming increasingly difficult, a problem which has come up in many branches of science.

John Davies and his associates at the University of Manchester have set up three receivers, one at the Jodrell Bank station and two more to the east and south about two and a half miles away. Echo signals detected at the east and south stations are automatically flashed by radio to the home receiver, and photographed together with the meteor signal it receives on a single film. The method furnishes rapid, three-dimensional pictures of a meteor's orbit in space and makes it possible to measure one such orbit every three seconds, twenty-four hours a day.

This is certainly an impressive feat. But things are getting a bit out of hand. Measuring devices are running far ahead of our ability to make sense of the measurements, and we may find ourselves buried beneath mountains of data that we shall never be able to study. It takes about six weeks to study the daily records of the three-receiver system, interpret the data and express them in astronomically meaningful terms. Six weeks of analysis for every day of measurement is a losing proposition. At that rate enough information is gathered in a single month to keep an investigator busy for more than three years.

In practice, of course, the trick is to select only some records for study and put the rest away in closets or file cabinets, the attics of scientific laboratories, for future reference. But this represents wasted information. Another alternative is to devise electronic methods of analyzing data. Davies has built a small calculating machine to help in the task. It digests data for a single meteor orbit in ten minutes—this used to take an hour and a half—and the information is then sent to a larger and faster electronic computer for further analysis. But still the three-receiver system can be used only part time, or else it would outrun both its designers and the calculating machine.

## HIGH-ALTITUDE DISTURBANCES

July, 1957, will mark a unique event in modern scientific research. It will be the start of an International Geophysical Year, a full twelve-month period devoted to a co-ordinated and intensive study of the earth and of remote bodies that influence conditions on earth. Scientists from almost every nation have made plans for three great chains of observing stations which will include existing laboratories as well as new outposts in the Arctic and Antarctic circles, the Sahara Desert, Africa, New Guinea, Tunisia and other places. The highly publicized and important satellite program, in which small man-made moons packed with scientific instruments will circle the earth, is part of the International Geophysical Year.

Many stations will make continuous observations of the sun (the sun-spot cycle will be entering a year of peak activity). Investigators will be studying Northern Lights and other atmospheric disturbances, cosmic rays, the movements of glaciers, ocean currents, terrestrial magnetic fields. Special photographs will be taken of the moon, planets and stars. Balloons equipped with automatic instruments will be released into the skies. Instrument-carrying rockets will rise from the ground, and from airplanes and launching balloons, to heights of 125 miles or more. Millions of measurements will be made in an effort to study man's physical and biological environment on a global basis.

Radar astronomy will play a leading part in research conducted during the International Geophysical Year. Electronic techniques being developed today will be used throughout the world. Meteor research, for example, offers new methods of observing tides and storms and turbulences high in the earth's atmosphere. The entire atmosphere weighs more than six million billion tons and three-quarters of that weight is concentrated in the lowest layer, which extends to about ten miles at its highest point. Our lives are affected by weather experienced at the very bottom of the layer. But conditions higher up, tens and hundreds of miles above this thin film of gases, are far more active and violent. They have a great deal to do with the weather we complain about, and the forecasts which are not fulfilled.

We have observed the upper atmosphere with telescopes and cameras which follow the motions of luminous clouds and other visible objects. Further evidence is furnished by sound waves reflected from high-altitude layers after surface explosions, and by rockets carrying measuring instruments. Now we are obtaining new information from studies of meteor echoes. The trail of electrified particles behind a flying meteor disappears as separated atomic fragments come together again and normal conditions are restored. Some trails last as much as half an hour. The great majority are gone after a tenth of a second.

But the trails move before they fade out. In a tenth of a second they may drift several miles, and they drift for the same reason that smoke drifts as it pours out of a factory smokestack. Meteor trails are swept along and dispersed by winds in the upper atmosphere. Modern radar methods of detecting them are reminiscent of the first records ever taken of high-blowing winds.

Nearly two thousand years ago Chinese observers noted how strong air currents moved the persistent and visible trails of unusually bright meteors or fireballs. Now we can look at radar screens as well as the skies, and instead of luminous trails in space we see glowing and wriggling lines, the impacts of electron beams made visible by fluorescent chemicals coated on the screens. When I watched a display of meteor echoes on a radar screen, they could be seen as sharp green pips or peaks which appeared and disappeared as the echoes died out. But some of the peaks changed before they vanished. They seemed to flicker slightly, to grow dimmer or brighter, and the variations in intensity indicate that upper-atmosphere winds are blowing the trails toward or away from the observing station.

Such winds exist fifty to seventy-five miles above the surface in the lower part of the ionosphere, a region containing ions or electrified atoms. Top speeds of more than 170 miles an hour have been recorded, although the average is about a mile a minute. According to Stanley Greenhow, of Jodrell Bank, this is how the winds behave on a typical September day: "At about midday the wind velocity is very low. The velocity then increases toward the north, swings round through the east and south, falling again to a very low value near midnight. The cycle repeats itself in the succeeding twelve hours." These and other observations may be traced to great ionospheric tides produced by the rising and setting sun.

Meteor echoes lasting considerably longer than a tenth of a second are also being studied for possible clues to the detailed structure of the ionosphere. Canadian investigators suggest that the lower parts of the region may be divided into layers, spaced roughly three to four miles apart. One radio astronomer, Edward Bowen, of the Australian group, believes that there is a significant connection between meteors and the weather. When the earth moves through meteor showers, many of the particles drift down into high clouds and, Bowen thinks, may act as "seeds," nuclei on which ice crystals form. The effect is similar to that claimed as a result of seeding experiments in which dry ice and other substances are dropped into suitable clouds to produce rain. Bowen has successfully predicted wet weather on the basis of his meteor-stream statistics.

Another method of probing the upper atmosphere does not depend on meteors or their echoes. It is a radio rather than a radar technique, and it tells us about conditions at much higher levels. When Hey and his associates discovered the Cygnus radio source ten years ago, they noted that the intensity of the signals varied in an irregular manner. In other words, the radio brightness is not constant but flickers like a fire. The radio star twinkles. Hey attributed the twinkling to violent disturbances in the source and compared them to sunspots.

Other investigators later confirmed the general facts, but arrived at a different interpretation. Australian workers observed the Cygnus source with two radio telescopes simultaneously. One instrument was in Sydney, and the other on the east coast of New Zealand, about twelve hundred miles away.

The idea was to check whether the twinkling of Cygnus was actually caused by flare-ups on the radio source. If so, changes of a signal strength in the radio star would be observed from widely separated stations on the earth. But if local conditions —conditions in the atmosphere of the earth—produced the changes, different signal patterns would be observed at different stations.

Cygnus studies indicated the correct answer. The intensity of signals from Cygnus varied at the two sites, but not in the same way. The intensity would rise in Sydney, and at the very same time either no increase or even a marked fading would be noted in New Zealand. Curves showing daily ups and downs as recorded at the two sites failed to fit. More refined experiments, conducted at Cambridge and Jodrell Bank in England, revealed that the twinkling of Cygnus was caused by the same general thing that causes the twinkling of visible stars—disturbances in the earth's atmosphere.

The disturbances consist of "irregularities," invisible sausage-shaped masses of electrons which may be more than fifteen miles long and which float in the upper atmosphere about two hundred and fifty miles above the surface of the earth. They produce twinkling as they pass across the lines of sight to Cygnus and other radio stars. They may move at velocities which exceed those of terrestrial hurricanes by a wide margin. An ordinary speed for the masses is more than four hundred miles an hour. But rocket-type speeds as high as twenty-four hundred miles an hour have been observed.

Allan Maxwell, formerly at the Jodrell Bank and now at Harvard, finds that the motion shifts peculiarly. In the first half of the night the prevailing direction is toward the west. Then around midnight the motion starts to shift to the opposite direction. According to a plausible theory, these disturbances can be traced to events lower down in the earth's atmosphere, at about the ninety-mile level. Here great atmospheric tides produce swift winds which blow clouds of electrified atomic particles about like sand in a sandstorm.

Wherever electrified particles flow, there are electric currents, and that is just what happens in the atmosphere. If the currents are strong enough, they set up electromagnetic forces resembling those that attract iron objects to an ordinary magnet. The result is that the forces produce disturbances higher up, disturbances that cause stars to twinkle. The nature of the disturbances is also a matter of theory. Maxwell believes they may be great turbulent eddies, swirling electron clouds. Research on the twinkling of radio stars is continuing, because it provides one of the few ways of studying the uppermost regions of the atmosphere.

We have already seen that in some cases "twinkling" may be the result of changes in the source itself. The fluctuating star reported by Ohio State investigators is one example. More recently O. B. Slee of Australia has found a source in Hydra, probably an extragalactic source, whose intensity varies in a period of six to twenty-four hours. It seems to brighten and dim in a definite rhythm. Such observations have not yet been explained.

Returning to observations based on radar methods, Northern Lights as well as meteors can give us information about conditions aloft. This research is going on in England, Norway, Sweden and Canada. In a field not far from the giant Jodrell Bank telescope is an aerial which resembles a group of television-type antennas and rotates completely like a ship's radar scanner. It has been running steadily for more than three years. Many things have been detected during the search—passing cars and airplanes, surrounding hills, and tens of thousands of meteors.

But Northern Lights, auroras, are the most spectacular events that appear on the viewing screen. Some of the images are almost as detailed as photographs. Streaks and irregular shapes, representing concentrations of matter hundreds of miles away, show up as bright patches of light which shift and flicker while you watch. Auroral displays, like meteor trails, can be seen by radar in broad daylight as well as after dark. One of the daytime displays appeared at a height of about seventy-five miles and extended for a thousand miles in a broad arc, a radar "rainbow," across the skies.

The radar echoes received from this aurora were reflected from disturbances moving along the arc, and moving at average speeds of some thirteen hundred miles an hour. (Top velocities as high as thirty-six hundred miles an hour have been recorded.) They cannot consist of trails like those marking the paths of meteors. Winds at that height blow far too slowly to keep the disturbances going at such enormous velocities. Investigators were observing the thing that makes the trail rather than the trail itself—and, judging by radar records alone, it cannot be identified.

But other research indicates the kind of trail-blazing agent being observed. Northern Lights are believed to be the result of discharges, electrical flashes or pulses, passing through great columns of gas in space. Exactly the same sort of thing happens in neon advertising signs and fluorescent lamps, which glow when streams of electricity shoot through gases enclosed in glass tubes. The flickering and wavering of Northern Lights are analogous to similar effects observed in such signs and lamps.

Radar echoes may be reflected from streams of electrified particles or waves passing through "neon tubes" in the skies. The particles presumably come from the sun.

During a period of low solar activity, which is when the Jodrell Bank studies were made, such streams may be emitted from sputtering regions on the turning sun, like water sprayed from the nozzles of a spinning garden sprinkler. In such peaceful times Northern Lights tend to occur at intervals of roughly twenty-seven days, the time required for one rotation of the sun. Since we are entering a period of intense sunspot and flare activity, we can expect more frequent displays of Northern Lights. There will be ample opportunity to use radar-echo methods in learning about the causes of glowing patterns in the skies.

## THE MOON AND BEYOND

Ten years ago a group of Army Signal Corps investigators succeeded in man's first deliberate attempt to make radar contact with the moon. The transmitting aerial had been set up on the coast of New Jersey, not far from the town of Holmdel, where Jansky discovered radio signals from the Milky Way. The radio engineer in charge of the tests was John DeWitt, at that time a lieutenant colonel and now president of a radio-television station in Nashville, Tennessee.

DeWitt used a standard radar set for the tests. In 1941 a previous model of the same type had given advance notice of Japanese airplanes coming in for the attack at Pearl Harbor. This set was modified to emit one pulse instead of thousands every five seconds. The outgoing pulse appeared as the usual flashing pip of light on the radar screen which, made audible over a loudspeaker, produced a sharp sound rather like a dog's yelp. About two and a half seconds later—the time it takes a radio pulse traveling with the speed of light to make the trip to and from the moon—the screen registered a smaller pip, and a fainter yelp was heard on the loudspeaker. Echoes continued to bounce back from the moon at the same regular intervals.

It was not the first time radar echoes had been received from the moon. Before and during the war investigators had picked up similar echoes in the course of tests conducted for other purposes. But the tests had always been secret, and this time the experiment was carefully planned and given wide publicity. Here are some of the headlines which appeared in the newspapers: RADAR HAS SCIENCE MOONSTRUCK WITH NOTIONS, MOON KICKS BACK RADAR AND NEW WORLD VISTA OPENS, RADAR ECHOES THROW LIGHT ON LUNAR RIDDLE. A Massachusetts Institute of Technology publication commented: "If we learn anything by howling at the moon, it is that man can expect to receive only that which he has produced."

Within a few months the experiment was repeated in Hungary. But that time the situation was somewhat similar to the one that existed after Jansky's discovery was first announced. After the publicity had died down, few persons seemed to know exactly what to make of moon radar and where to go next. But about two years later Frank Kerr, C. A. Shain and C. S. Higgins of the Radiophysics Laboratory in Australia undertook tests on the basis of a significant finding in the Signal Corps research.

Not all the army's echoes came back at full strength. Many of them were appreciably fainter than had been expected, and sometimes no signals were received at all. In seeking to explain such fade-outs the Australians turned to the only appreciable concentration of matter between the surfaces of the moon and the earth, the earth's atmosphere. Perhaps the effects were caused by disturbances in the upper regions of the ionosphere, which cannot be observed directly from the surface. If so, it might be possible to study these regions by sending signals whose lunar echoes came down through them from above.

To check their theory the group at the Radiophysics Laboratory performed experiments at an existing station, Radio Australia, which broadcasts regularly to the United States and Canada. They used the station's aerials to send powerful radio pulses to the moon, and received the echoes with a set located several hundred miles away. Their early experiments, while not conclusive, suggested a definite connection between long echo fade-outs and activity in the uppermost layers of the ionosphere. Early one morning, for example, the reflected signals were lost for half an hour during an ionospheric disturbance.

In similar experiments at Jodrell Bank more than a hundred thousand moon echoes have been received and analyzed. The English results generally confirm those reported from Australia. Apparently radio waves bounce off the moon and are affected by the earth's magnetic field as they pass through the ionosphere. The work is continuing with the hope of eventually measuring the concentration of electrons in regions several hundred miles above the surface, and perhaps determining their shape and extent.

Broadcasting companies are among those which stand to benefit directly from the research. A better understanding of these regions, for example, would make it possible to forecast radio conditions more precisely and further in advance. In broadcasts across the Atlantic and Pacific oceans, radio waves are bounced from electrified layers in the ionosphere. The height of the layers changes, and good transmission and reception depend on selecting the right wave lengths for different altitude variations. Such problems are involved when the World Series and other events are broadcast to troops overseas, and in other long-distance operations.

Investigators at many radio observatories are also interested in making radar contact with more remote objects. One of the major problems is the design of sufficiently powerful transmitters. The sun, for example, is about four hundred times further away than the moon, which means its echoes would be 160,000 times weaker—and the original pulses would have to be a great deal more intense. But the past few years have seen significant advances in the electronics of transmitters. New television tubes constructed in American industrial laboratories can transmit at levels of three hundred thousand watts or better—the original Signal Corps instrument was only about a hundredth as powerful—and could be modified to produce the sort of pulses required for interplanetary signals.

Detecting the signals is another problem. Receivers not only have to be sensitive, they must also remain extraordinarily "quiet." If you are straining to hear something a considerable distance away, you do not want people making noise nearby. The chronic noise inherent in radio receivers is equally annoying. Although it is not really very loud, it may be louder than faint radar signals. If it happens to come at the same time as an echo from some distant celestial object, the signal may be completely drowned out.

Receiver noise can be controlled by properly designed circuits, but special circuits are required to attain silent periods of longer than ten or twenty seconds. Serious difficulties do not arise for moon echoes, which return within three seconds. Planetary echoes take a good deal longer, however. It would be necessary to wait four minutes and thirty-five seconds for signals from Venus, and the round trip from Saturn to the earth requires about two hours and twenty minutes. (Even if sufficient power were available, say, a thousand billion watts, it would be out of the question to wait more than three years for echoes from the nearest star.)

Within the limitations of present-day techniques, Mars offers one of the most attractive targets. In 1924 engineers at station WOR in New York tried sending radio waves to the planet, and according to one reporter's story, the signals were received and messages flashed back to earth from wide-awake Martians. The story turned out to be a hoax. Fifteen years later

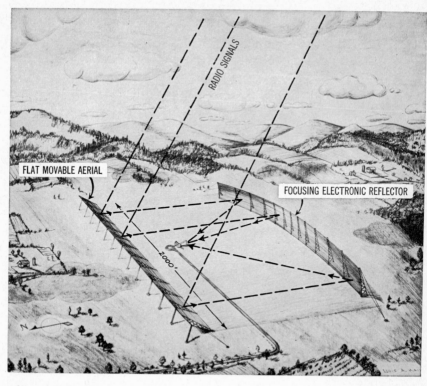

Giant radio telescope proposed by John Kraus, of Ohio
State University.

Actual small-scale model of Kraus's telescope.

The expanding universe . . . a rapidly inflating balloon . . .

WOR engineers tried again, again without success. Anyway, if the arguments of certain astronomers prove correct, we should not expect to establish communications with intelligent living things on Mars. Life there, if any, may not have reached an advanced stage of evolution and the highest organisms may be relatively primitive.

But planetary echoes may be received in the near future, because our equipment is so much better. The 250-foot aerial of the Jodrell Bank radio telescope could be used to send out high-power pulses produced by special transmitters. It could also detect the echoes, which would require about nine minutes to travel from the earth to Mars and back. Astronomers are interested in such research mainly for one reason. Precise timing of the echoes would permit us to measure the distance to Mars more accurately than ever before, and that distance could be used to recalculate the scale of the entire solar system. Present measurements are accurate to about one part in a thousand, and radar-echo studies might improve this figure by a factor of ten to a hundred.

Echoes from Venus, another promising target, might clear up a long-standing problem. Although Venus is believed to require about a month to make one rotation on its axis, the precise period is still not known. A cloudy atmosphere hides its surface and contains no permanent markings to follow. But radar pulses penetrating the clouds would strike the surface, and be deflected and scattered like streams of water hitting a spinning globe. The amount of scattering would provide an indication of the rate of spin.

Frank Kerr and other members of the Australian group have considered the possibility of sending radar signals to the sun. Echoes would follow transmitted pulses by about sixteen minutes, and receiver noise is not the chief problem in detecting them. Of far greater importance is possible interference from the sun's own radio waves and those emitted by the Milky Way. If these difficulties are overcome, and Kerr is convinced they can be, we will have a new way of studying movements and disturbances in the outer corona—and perhaps the streams of outgoing particles which cause Northern Lights and magnetic storms on earth.

After we have established radar contacts with the sun and the most accessible planets, it will be only a matter of time before someone puts them to use. Specialists in space travel are discussing methods of navigating by interplanetary radar. Bernard Lovell, who heads the Jodrell Bank station, has reviewed science-fiction books and contributed a few futuristic ideas of his own. For one thing, he believes that spaceships might be guided by beams of radar pulses from Mars, using blind-flying systems somewhat like those operating at terrestrial airports. The beams would be emitted by giant parabolic aerials located at strategic points on earth or on artificial satellites.

Another new application may come sooner. The International Telephone and Telegraph Company has already considered long-distance communications by radar echoes. The moon would serve as the side cushion of a great celestial billiard table. Signals from any point on earth would be reflected back over all parts of the earth facing the moon at the time of transmission. They could be used in transatlantic telephone service or in television.

Many radio engineers believe that moon-radar communications would suffer less from interference than the ordinary variety. Since modern broadcasting depends on bouncing signals off the ionosphere, we must use long waves. Short waves would not be reflected by the ionosphere, and would pass through and out into space. But static tends to be much worse at longer wave lengths—whether it comes from airplane ignition systems, vacuum cleaners or thunderstorms. These difficulties might be greatly reduced in moon or planetary communications which would use short-wave, low-static channels.

But perhaps the most important advances of the future will be ones we cannot foresee today. A great deal of attention has been paid to the discovery and identification of radio stars and to other projects which concentrate on radio waves emitted by objects in outer space. The full use of pulses produced on earth has awaited the development of powerful transmitters and new aerials. Now that such equipment is available, we can look forward to a spurt of activity in all phases of radar astronomy.

# 14

## THE FUTURE

Few things are more impressive than the skies and the stars at night. We look upward and feel distance and immensity, and the existence of worlds among and beyond the lights that are suns. We also feel a vast calm. The stars and the constellations are in their places. We shall not see the patterns changing in our lifetimes, and it seems that here is the stability and order which we may not find elsewhere.

The feeling of distance and immensity is an intuitive expression of what we have found by observing. The feeling of calm, of things having settled down, is an illusion. Most of the advances we have discussed represent work conducted during the last decade. Many of them have come within the last year or two. And they all confirm and extend the notion that the universe is restless, restless beyond anything we can imagine and restless in the same fundamental sense that living things are restless. Restlessness is built into the nature of the universe, into the very nature of existence.

Our sun, long known as a blazing nuclear furnace, is also a source of intense radio storms and outbursts. Even its coldest satellites may storm and seethe and emit massive bolts of radio lightning. Similar violence is found on a galactic scale.

Abundant radio signals reach us from places where stars are being born and taking on new structures, from exploding stars, from the tenuous streamers of gas that make up the arms of the spinning Milky Way, from gas and dust clouds and nebulae, and clusters of distant blue-hot suns. Those signals indicate that our star system has the form of a spiral, an ancient symbol of motion and restlessness.

Radio astronomy takes us beyond the Milky Way, through the remotest corridors of space and into regions of activity never before observed. Outer galaxies, island universes, are found to be less isolated than is commonly believed. Like the stars, they may be part of superclusters. They move and come close and collide. And when they collide, the impact produces the enormously powerful radio waves we listen to on earth. Furthermore, some of the Milky Ways in the universe seem to be connected with one another. There are intergalactic wisps and filaments, and we hope in time to trace them and interpret their meaning.

In this chapter we shall be considering instruments which do not yet exist and observations which have not yet been made. They represent the plans and speculations of leaders in the new science of radio astronomy, investigators looking ahead to the research that they and their students will be doing within the next generation or so. Their predictions may or may not be verified, and the future of any active branch of science cannot be spelled out in detail. The only sure thing is that we shall continue to learn for some time to come, for millions of years at least, and that the universe will open wide in the process.

## NEW RADIO TELESCOPES

A sign of the looking ahead, of the anticipation of studies which are not yet possible, is the wealth of schemes and blueprints for new observing instruments. At present the Big Dish in England is a lonely giant, like the first pyramid or the first skyscraper. But soon other giants will be available for use in a scientific drive to obtain more information about the universe.

More than two years ago Edward Bowen traveled from the Radiophysics Laboratory in Sydney to Washington, D.C. He had made several appointments. There were certain Weather Bureau records to be examined as evidence for his theory about meteors and rainfall. He also met officials of the Carnegie Institution and discussed plans for expanding what is already the world's largest radio observatory. Some time later the Institution announced that it was giving the Sydney laboratory $250,000 to help with the building of a new radio telescope, another 250-foot dish which will be supported by additional funds from the Australian government.

In the United States, plans for large-scale building projects are taking shape at laboratories on the east and west coasts. From the California Institute of Technology, which operates the 200-inch optical telescope on Mount Palomar, Jesse Greenstein writes a restrained "we will build some rather large equipment." Construction of a giant radio telescope is already under way there; it will be a twin-aerial instrument or interferometer consisting of two 80-foot dishes mounted on vertical railroad tracks.

The new telescope, which is being built with navy funds, will be used in many projects. For one thing, it is designed to obtain extra-precise positions of unidentified radio stars and help discover what they actually are. To head its radio-astronomy program the Institute has imported from Australia John Bolton, the first investigator to identify a radio star with a known celestial object, the Crab Nebula.

Scientists in New York and Washington are considering an even more ambitious program. The idea, which is currently being considered in detail, is to organize a large new radio observatory for the use of a group of universities. It would include a 140-foot telescope to start with, but instruments as much as 600 feet in diameter may be erected eventually. The observatory may be located in a Blue Ridge Mountain region including parts of Tennessee, Kentucky, Virginia and West Virginia. Weather Bureau records indicate that for some reason this great oval region has never had hurricanes or tornadoes, an important point in choosing a site for high dish-shaped aerials.

Research is also increasing at Harvard, Stanford University —which has imported another Australian, R. C. Bracewell— and other institutions. Such work will insure that the United States, where Jansky and Reber conducted their pioneer studies, will rank high among world leaders in radio astronomy.

Radio telescopes will be getting bigger and bigger, and the end is not in sight. Some time ago I was talking with Bernard Lovell in his Jodrell Bank office. The Big Dish was not completed then. In fact, the great bowl had not been started; engineers were considering various methods of putting the radio reflector together. Lovell had just returned from a brief vacation to face new problems and worries in the long task of seeing the project through to a finish. Yet he still found time to think about future telescopes which would dwarf his unfinished giant: "We can see some of the things we will be doing. Some day we shall have radio observatories which occupy hundreds of acres. They will include enormous telescopes, half a mile to a mile in diameter."

"Some day" may not be far off. Detailed diagrams for supertelescopes are already in existence. Of course, reflectors half a mile or a mile across—ten to twenty city blocks—will not be tiltable like the bowl of the Big Dish. It would be impractical to design such structures for sweeping the horizon like searchlights. Consequently, they will be somewhat muscle-bound.

At each given position an aerial is most sensitive to signals received from a certain region in outer space, and is said to be "beamed" to that region. The reception beam of these supertelescopes will be shifted to another region by electronic methods. The aerial itself will not be shifted. But this method does not permit us to cover as much territory as actual tilting, so supertelescopes will survey smaller portions of the skies. They probably will not look like present-day instruments, either. The differences in shape and design will be as radical as those between the Wright brothers' Kitty Hawk plane and a modern jet fighter with swept-back wings.

To cite only one example, John Kraus at Ohio State University has worked out the principles for an unusual mammoth telescope. In a preliminary sketch it resembles an architect's drawing for a new type of open-air arena. Radio waves from space strike a flat tiltable aerial nearly half a mile long and wider than a superhighway. The waves bounce off the aerial surface, travel parallel to the ground and strike the side of a fixed vertical reflector, a great electronic mirror which is curved and stands about twenty stories high. The mirror focuses the signals so that they flow into a receiver set up somewhere between the two structures.

This system, of which a small working model has already been built, is a highly efficient trap for radio waves. It will catch and focus signals falling on an area of about 400,000 square feet or ten acres, which is considerably larger than that of any instrument in existence today (the Big Dish and Martin Ryle's Cambridge telescopes gather waves falling on about an acre of aerial surface). Kraus's radio telescope will be fantastically sensitive. It will detect signals too faint for present-day equipment, and its range will be extended proportionately. It will be focused more sharply and is expected to discover a large number of new radio stars.

A dramatic advance is almost certain to come with the development of large, sharp-focus radio telescopes. Objects in the radio skies will become less blurred. Instead of seeing them all at once, as well as extensive regions of surrounding space, we shall be able to examine them part by part. In a similar manner the Palomar telescope does not look at the moon as a whole. Its magnifying power is so great that it observes only a small section of the lunar surface at a time.

Sharper focusing offers the exciting possibility of observing radio stars directly. Nowadays we must deduce their shape and appearance mainly from the inked markings on typical chart-paper records. Tomorrow we will actually see radio stars, on large television screens. Radio telescopes will be used as television cameras. They will scan small sections of invisible transmitting centers in outer space and transform the signals into varying intensities of light on a fluorescent screen —then blend them all together into a single composite image.

Words cannot describe the things we are waiting to see. The prospect is even more intriguing if we try to imagine color television, radio stars in Technicolor. The Orion and Whirlpool and Great Loop nebulae in the Milky Way will appear as

*. . . tomorrow we may actually "see" radio stars on large television screens . . .*

great swirling clouds in new forms. The Crab Nebula, the tangled remains of an exploding star, may have a shape radically different from that observed by conventional telescopes, which do not necessarily show the places emitting the strongest radio signals. Intense signals may be coming from the dark regions between the arches and wisps and filaments of the powerful radio source in Cassiopeia, and our radio-television telescopes may reveal strange formations and structures in the skies.

Beyond the Milky Way we will see a new Andromeda. We should be able to view the beautiful spiral by radio light, but we should also see the spiral surrounded by its great shell or halo, and perhaps watch the entire object flicker like Northern Lights. We may obtain detailed pictures of the colliding galaxies in Cygnus. We know that the nuclei of the two star systems are distorted by gravitational attraction, that the impact must produce enormous splashes and jet streams of luminous gases. It may be only a matter of time before we see all this with our own eyes.

As far as such objects are concerned we can make guesses, however inadequate, about what might be seen on television screens. The objects have been identified with visible bodies, and our guesses are based partly on observations of those bodies. But most radio stars remain unidentified because the disturbances which give rise to their broadcasts cannot be seen with lenses and mirrors. When we televise these mysterious objects, we shall be literally seeing the invisible. We shall be probing the most elusive portions of the radio skies, examining events that our eyes could never observe without the aid of electronics. In the observatories of the future radio astronomers will tune in on the radio universe, selecting regions and objects the way we select television channels at home.

## WAR AND PEACE

Radio astronomy has many possible uses, and most of the ones we have mentioned concern developments of interest in times of peace. Research on radio navigation is a case in point. All we have now is a few models of early-style radio sextants which take bearings by radio signals from the sun and moon. Within a decade, however, ocean liners and merchant ships and airline planes may be steering with the aid of new instruments. Advances can also be expected in our understanding of disturbances on the sun and in the ionosphere, and the advances will bring improved radio and television reception throughout the world.

But science is a double-edged thing whose value in war as well as in peace has been demonstrated over and over again. It is worth pointing out that in this respect science is no different from any other sort of human activity. The intelligence agent who risks his life behind enemy lines, the professional mountain-climber who leads a daring commando raid, the chaplain who speaks of God and faith to troops entering battle—these and many other specialists are contributing to a nation's war effort as definitely as the investigator in the laboratory. The investigator is not a legitimate target for extra approbation because his work may be better publicized and, in some cases, more spectacular.

One possible military application of radio astronomy is a natural outgrowth of engineering studies in radio navigation. If ships can be steered by signals from the skies, so can guided missiles. Some information has been released about a new Air Force rocket called Atlas. The rocket can carry an enormous load of atomic or conventional explosives, and deliver it to remote targets. Its speed is said to be "at least" ten thousand miles an hour, which means it could fly from New York to Chicago in better than two and a half minutes. Its range has not been revealed, but it is known as an intercontinental ballistics missile."

The Atlas contains built-in electronic equipment which enables it to steer itself to its target, and it is one of the first missiles to steer by celestial navigation. Although details have not been published, this could work somewhat as follows. Assume the rocket is to be launched at midnight for a target across the Atlantic Ocean, and contains a compact high-speed electronic calculating machine. Before its launching, technicians would insert a cartridge of magnetic tape, the sort used in making sound recordings, into a special part of the machine. Flight instructions are "written" on the tape, in the form of a code of magnetized spots which the machine can read while the rocket is in passage.

The code furnishes complete details about step-by-step progress on the desired course. Specifically, it provides the exact positions of the stars Atlas is to go by. As the rocket moves through space, the computer automatically observes the stars with special photoelectric cells, "electronic eyes" like those that open swinging doors as you pass through. It repeatedly compares the rocket's actual position with the positions specified in the coded instructions and corrects any deviations by sending signals to the steering mechanism. One of the most closely guarded secrets is the nature of this Air Force equipment and its target-striking accuracy.

Atlas steers by starlight. But there is no reason why later models of intercontinental rockets should not use radio waves from the sun or the moon—or radio stars. Instead of photoelectric cells they would carry aerials, the wave-gathering elements of radio telescopes. The first models at least would probably be guided by star signals at the short-wave end of the radio spectrum. The detection of longer wave lengths usually calls for large aerials which would be far too bulky for guided missiles. On the other hand, the Air Force is already experimenting with small aerials for other purposes and they might be useful in picking up short-wave signals generated by various transmitters in the skies.

A rocket taking its bearings from such signals could keep track of any one of a number of radio stars. The Great Nebula in Orion, for example, broadcasts intensely at very short wave lengths—in fact, as we have already emphasized, the shorter the wave length the more powerful its signals. So guided missiles might speed toward their targets using information from one of the most prolific stellar breeding places in the Milky Way. Other radio stars whose signals are powerful at short wave lengths include the Crab Nebula, the colliding Cygnus galaxies, the Cassiopeia source, and an unidentified object in the constellation of the Archer.

Radio telescopes may help to detect as well as steer guided missiles, a fact of which military officials are well aware. The Big Dish at Jodrell Bank and other instruments can be used as radar antennas to bounce signals off any object within a large radius. A meteor, a natural missile, flashes through a region of the atmosphere at a rate of more than 150,000 miles an hour. Yet observers on earth, some six hundred miles away, can detect it and locate its position with high accuracy. The equipment which makes this feat possible can certainly detect slower-moving and considerably larger man-made missiles at much greater distances. It is a good guess that such equipment is playing a part in the nation's defense plans.

But this is simply a refinement of methods used in World War II. It may be possible to follow missiles, and aircraft, by listening to the radio waves they emit. Radar techniques require echoes and powerful transmitters which may not be absolutely necessary in the future. The engines that drive rockets and bombers, or the objects themselves as they speed through the skies, may create radio signals which radio telescopes could pick up. In other words, our missiles and aircraft may be radio sources more feeble but otherwise not unlike those of outer space. We should be able to treat them as such, deduce their shapes and motions, and perhaps even see them on television screens hooked up to radio telescopes.

Another possibility involves an entirely different sort of military problem, detecting the experimental explosion of new atomic and hydrogen bombs. Most of what we know about nuclear weapons tested at proving grounds in the Soviet Union comes from samples of air containing radioactive materials. The materials originate in the mushroom-shaped clouds, rise into the upper atmosphere and are blown to regions all over the world by high and fast winds. The analysis of such air samples can yield a surprising amount of information about bombs detonated thousands of miles away.

But the method is not infallible, and observers at sampling stations in and outside of the United States could be deceived. It is conceivable that immediately before or after a test explosion large airplanes loaded with materials from other sources—say, from the waste products of atomic-energy factories—might succeed in dumping appreciable quantities of radioactive chemicals into the skies. If this could be done, spotters might have a trying time analyzing their air samples. They might confuse the added substances with those produced by a bomb and draw false conclusions.

A radio telescope would be more difficult to fool. Atomic bombs emit radio waves along with light, gamma rays and other radiations. Perhaps by choosing the proper wave lengths w: could tune in on such signals. In the discussion of radio sources in the Milky Way, it was indicated that a supernova may be a nuclear weapon of cosmic dimensions, since its energy is equivalent to that of billions and billions of hydrogen bombs. We can also look at things the other way around. In a sense a hydrogen bomb is a man-made supernova. To be sure, it is not nearly as powerful, but—and this is the important point—the explosion takes place a great deal closer to our radio telescopes, on the earth itself.

That means the hydrogen bomb may generate signals considerably more powerful than those which can be produced by radio or television broadcasting stations. Could we tune in on such nuclear signals, as we do with radio stars? No one will talk about the possibility, for publication or even off the record. But one thing is clear. If the possibility exists, it is being explored. No military group can afford to ignore a chance to keep tabs on nuclear developments of other nations, and to develop effective spotting techniques which might help discourage a world-wide atomic conflict.

It is also clear that any one of these developments can be turned to peaceful purposes. Radio methods of steering and detecting missiles could guide intercontinental, or interplanetary, rockets carrying passengers and mail and other cargoes. Atomic energy itself may ultimately be used to generate superpowerful radio waves for communications around and beyond the earth. If science is expected to justify its existence with an array of practical achievements, there is little doubt that radio astronomy will earn its keep.

## THE NATURE OF THE UNIVERSE

The most ambitious objective of astronomy, perhaps the most ambitious objective of human knowledge, is to understand our place in the scheme of things. The deepest questions of all concern the universe as a whole, rather than its individual galaxies with their suns and satellites and satellites of satellites. It happens that studies of the origin and fate of the universe have been somewhat in the doldrums recently. There have been plenty of theories, and the list of possible universes is long and impressive, but we have come up against obstacles in our efforts to prove or disprove them, to establish any single one as the most valid. Many theories call for a wealth of precise observations of objects which lie at or beyond the limits of the Palomar telescope and other optical instruments.

Radio astronomy may help significantly in solving present-day problems, or in eliminating certain theories and clearing away the deadwood. For example, it may help us decide between two broad concepts of the nature of the physical universe—the "cosmic egg" theory and the theory of continuous creation. Both concepts start with the notion that the universe is expanding. This notion is still open to some doubt, but most astronomers agree that it jibes with the facts we have so far. It is based on observations gathered during the past forty years and extended by a study of nearly eight hundred galaxies which has just been completed at the Mount Wilson and Mount Palomar observatories.

Wherever we look beyond the Milky Way and the cluster of star systems to which it belongs, we see island universes in retreat. They are retreating at enormous rates, up to tens of thousands of miles a second. Certain galaxies in the direction of the constellation Gemini are about 1,300,000,000 miles further away today than they were yesterday, and all outer galaxies seem to be receding in a similar way although at different rates. The universe is apparently a rapidly inflating balloon, so that its parts, viewed from any point in the interior, are moving off into space.

Up to this point the two theories are in general agreement. From here on they part company. The cosmic-egg theory is based on the fact that, mathematically speaking, we can deflate the balloon. We can run the reel backward as it were. Taking the observed recession rates, investigators have calculated how long the galaxies must have been retreating to reach their present positions—and where they must have started from.

According to one such calculation, they were all in roughly the same general region about four to six billion years ago. At that time the matter now found in galaxies and the spaces between them existed in the form of a "nuclear fluid." One cubic inch of the superdense fluid weighed considerably more than all the warships in all the world's navies. It was concentrated in a relatively small volume. The entire substance of the observable universe may have been jammed together into a sphere less than eight hundred million miles across, a mere speck compared with the dimensions of the universe we know today.

That sphere is the cosmic egg. The egg hatched violently some billions of years ago. It exploded with a blast that heralded the coming of galaxies and suns. The nuclear fluid turned to gas as the shell of original matter grew larger and larger, and the entire system is expanding still. The front of the shell, the material of the outer edge, moves out through space at breakneck speed—a vast wave rolling on like heavy surf. It has been suggested that we can listen in to the extragalactic surf. Part of the background signals we pick up with radio telescopes, the messages that come in from regions where we have found no radio stars, may be produced by the shock-wave front of the expanding universe.

Current versions of the cosmic-egg theory have many implications. For one thing, as the galaxies retreat they pass out of the range of our most powerful telescopes. To keep up with the present rates of expansion we would have to double the size of our observing instruments every two or three billion years. Eventually all star systems will have disappeared from our skies. The Milky Way and its handful of companion galaxies will be all that we can observe of the aging and expanding universe.

Abbé Lemaître, the Belgium astronomer who first proposed the cosmic egg more than a generation ago, expresses it as follows: "The evolution of the world can be compared to a display of fireworks that has just ended; some few red wisps, ashes and smoke. Standing on a well-chilled cinder, we see the slow fading of the suns, and we try to recall the vanished brilliance of the origin of the worlds."

The theory of continuous creation differs radically from Lemaître's hypothesis. It holds out no such sad prospects. According to Fred Hoyle and other advocates of the theory, our skies will never be empty of galaxies. To be sure, galaxies now within telescopic range will disappear because they are retreating. But new ones will take their places. Matter is breeding, replenishing itself at just the right rate to compensate for the escaping substance that vanishes as the universe expands.

The rate is exceedingly slow. In a space about the size of your living room a brand-new hydrogen atom appears every four or five thousand years. But since the process is going on throughout the observable universe, the total amount of matter is somewhat more impressive—some 1,000,000,000,000,000,-000,000,000,000,000,000 tons, the weight of fifty thousand suns, coming into existence every second. The way creation works is a complete mystery, as in the cosmic-egg theory. We can say the new matter arises from energy, a phenomenon already observed on an infinitesimally small scale in experiments with atom-smashing machines. That only leads to deeper mysteries. We have no idea where the energy comes from.

But the new theory offers an unusual and original version of creation. The process did not start as a single dramatic act with a great explosion or any other sort of catastrophe. We are not viewing the final stages of an event which is over and done with, and may never be observed again. Creation is going on all the time. If we accept this idea, we have to accept something else which is also part of the logic of the theory.

We are not to think of the universe in terms of birth and maturing and death, notions which necessarily apply to ourselves and our experiences. Go back in time as far as you like, and you always find a wide and varied population of objects in the skies. The universe has always existed and it will always exist. There is no such thing as creation in the usual sense. Infinity lies at the core of things.

The idea of continuous creation can be checked, a necessary feature of truly scientific theories. This fact distinguishes it from the cosmic-egg hypothesis (it would be impossible to disprove or prove the notion that an explosion occurred billions of years ago). Matter is being created far too slowly to measure, but there is another way of examining the validity of the theory—and radio astronomers have been among the first to put it to the test.

In part of his new survey at Cambridge, Martin Ryle has studied the positions of nearly two thousand radio stars. The stars of the sample population lie in all directions about the sun, and an analysis of how they are distributed leads to important conclusions. The most plausible deduction is that they are scattered through a vast spherical portion of space whose radius is at least 650,000,000 light-years. In other words, the dimensions of the sphere are comparable to those of the observable universe.

But radio stars are not located uniformly among the galaxies. Ryle reports that the intensity of recorded radio signals is such that more and more broadcasting sources are encountered at greater and greater distances. The density, or perhaps the brightness, of radio stars increases as you travel increasingly far from the earth. This finding is in direct contradiction to a basic assumption of continuous-creation proponents. Their theory states that the universe is "homogeneous," that galaxies and intergalactic matter are distributed evenly throughout space. Of course, there are exceptional concentrations, such as clusters of galaxies, but if you consider large enough portions of space, local irregularities are not significant.

The possibility that the density of radio stars increases with distance, however, does not fit in with this concept. If Ryle is correct, nearby and remote parts of space differ markedly in the amount of material they contain. The idea of a universe everywhere the same would have to go, and the continuous-creation theory would probably go with it. The issue is not yet settled. The Cambridge survey is the first of its kind ever completed and there will be other surveys, notably in the United States and at Jodrell Bank and Sydney. But indications are that radio-star studies will have a great deal to do with shaping our theories about the nature of things.

Another research frontier is an extensive exploration of the expanding universe with radio telescopes. Our new listening posts will almost certainly reveal facts about receding galaxies that elude us now.

Evidence for the expanding universe rests on an effect known as the red-shift. We have already come across a similar effect in studies of interstellar hydrogen at 21-centimeter wave lengths. The whistle of a locomotive moving away sounds lower, its wave length is longer, than if the locomotive were standing still or approaching. Radio waves received from retreating hydrogen clouds are also lengthened, and so are light waves from retreating galaxies. Light waves appear longer, redder, from every single one of the hundreds of outer galaxies studied for this effect. There are no exceptions to the red-shift, and that fact represents our strongest proof that the universe is inflating.

But we are reaching a limit beyond which the red-shift can no longer help us. Imagine a light spectrum stretching in a broad band on a screen. All the colors of the rainbow appear in front of you, in the conventional order. To your left is the violet end of the spectral band. Then follow blue, green, yellow and orange. Red comes at the other end, to your right. Now if the band were accelerated away from you at thousands of miles a second, and if you could still see it, all the colors in the band would change. At the left the violet light would appear longer and bluer, the blue light next to it would appear greener, and so on.

The most significant change, however, comes at the other end of the band, to your extreme right. The red light there also becomes longer. But in this case you do not observe the changed wave length. Red waves have turned to infrared waves, heat waves which we cannot see. Part of the spectral band, the part at the extreme right, has become invisible. The same general kind of thing happens when astronomers observe a retreating galaxy.

But the faster a galaxy retreats, the greater the red-shift. At some velocity many colors of the spectrum become so much longer that they all register as infrared rays, invisible radiation. In other words, a large portion of the light spectrum, the most intense portion, has vanished. Although special photographic film sensitive to infrared rays may help us detect some of the invisible radiations, galaxies retreating faster than a certain speed cannot be observed by photographic techniques. The speed is about one-third the speed of light, or sixty-two thousand miles a second, which is just about the point where the recession of galaxies begins to get interesting.

Radio astronomy offers the possibility of detecting another kind of red-shift, and reaching further than ever into the expanding universe. Galaxies emit a spectrum of radio as well as light waves, and soon we may be observing radio red-shifts routinely from objects far beyond the range of present-day telescopes. As we know from studies of hydrogen-cloud broadcasts, the waves become longer as the source retreats faster.

A recent report from the Naval Research Laboratory hints at the nature of future observations. Lilley and McLain have detected the first radio red-shift. They focused the laboratory's fifty-foot aerial on an object lying vast distances outside our Milky Way, the colliding galaxies in Cygnus 260,000,000 light-years away. Their sensitive receiver was designed to pick up radio waves generated by hydrogen atoms in turbulent gases at the scene of this remote collision.

Hydrogen signals came in clearly—but not at 21 centimeters, the wave length which would have been expected from a stationary source. The waves were longer, which indicates that the hydrogen-containing source is retreating. Not only that, but the increase in wave length, the radio red-shift, was thousands of times greater than any increases observed for clouds in the spiral arms of our own Milky Way. This means that the Cygnus galaxies are retreating at a much higher speed than the clouds.

Lilley and McLain calculate from their radio measurements that the Cygnus source is moving away from us at about 10,-500 miles a second, a finding which checks with optical calculations by Baade and Minkowski in California. This is further evidence that the universe is expanding, and these new results are only the beginning.

Looking through the new window to space, we should be able to study galaxies receding at nine-tenths the speed of light or more. Since the galaxies with the highest recession rates are also the most distant, that means we would be looking into new, remote territories. We might finally measure the shape and dimensions of the universe. One deduction from Einstein's general theory of relativity is that space curves back on itself, forming a kind of closed system. If you could travel long enough out through the galaxies, you would come back to your starting point. You would return at last to the Milky Way, and to the sun and its satellite earth. It would be the cosmic equivalent of circumnavigating the globe.

To determine whether space is curved in this or some other way we must observe over vast distances, and we must have a bird's-eye view. Similarly, the curvature of the earth is best seen in photographs taken from rockets far above the surface. Some years ago Edwin Hubble, using the 100-inch Mount Wilson telescope, believed he had actually succeeded in measuring the curvature of the universe. Now we know that his observations were in error. Even the 200-inch Mount Palomar telescope may not be powerful enough to gather the facts we need.

Astronomers have considered building a still bigger instrument, but the project may not be necessary. Radio telescopes may serve the purpose better. If they reveal fewer galaxies with increasing distance, if the galaxies thin out in a certain way, we shall have strong evidence that space curves around like the earth's surface. If the galaxies become more dense, space may not be curving "downward," but may have a different shape. We might be looking at a great rising slope, the side of a plateau in the cosmos. Perhaps Martin Ryle's new findings hint at some such discovery.

## TO THE EDGE OF SPACE

We have excellent reasons to believe that our radio telescopes can probe deep into the universe, deeper than optical telescopes. The reasons involve a spectacular radio source, the colliding galaxies in the direction of the Cygnus constellation. The galaxies are barely observable by optical methods. They make only a faint smudge on Mount Palomar photographs, because they lie close to the observing limits of the great 200-inch instrument, the largest conventional telescope in the world.

But the same colliding galaxies which shine so feebly for Palomar observers are enormously bright in radio light. Their extra-intense radio signals produce large and clear-cut patterns on our recording instruments. Present-day radio telescopes could readily detect an object whose broadcasts were only one four-hundredth as intense as those of the Cygnus source. To put it another way, we could observe the source if it were twenty times more distant. Its estimated distance is about 260,000,000 light-years. That gives a good radio telescope a possible range of 5,200,000,000 light-years, which is more than two and a half times the range of the Palomar giant.

Radio telescopes of the future will be even more powerful. Kraus's half-mile "arena" telescope, for example, would have an incredible range if we go by similar calculations. The Ohio State investigator estimates that it could detect objects one ten-thousandth as intense as the Cygnus source. An object might be observed at a distance of sixty billion light-years. We could explore a volume of space much larger than that being explored today, an extension represented by the difference between a marble and the dome of St. Peter's.

Such ranges may be all we can ever use. In fact, if current ideas are correct, most of the extra power of new radio telescopes will be worthless as far as observing further is concerned. The observable universe may have an "edge," an outer limit beyond which we can never see. The all-important fact that the most distant galaxies in the expanding universe are the ones retreating fastest leads to a startling conclusion.

One of the slowest galaxies lies 6,000,000 light-years away in the direction of the Virgo constellation. It is receding at a rate of 700 miles a second. A galaxy in Pegasus is further away, 23,000,000 light-years, and its recession is 3,400 miles a second. The most rapidly retreating galaxy yet observed is 360,000,000 light-years from us and moves away at a speed of 38,000 miles a second. It follows that as we look further into space we shall come across increasingly remote galaxies, retreating at higher and higher velocities. At some distance, which works out to about four billion light-years or twice the range of the Palomar telescope, there should be galaxies retreating at the speed of light itself, 186,000 miles a second.

This is the end of our calculations, and possibly the end of our efforts to set new astronomical distance records. We could never observe a galaxy four billion light-years away. Its radiation, light waves and radio waves and all, would never reach us.

Look at the second hand of your watch. It ticks off one position, and during that second radiations from the far-off galaxy travel 186,000 miles. But during the same instant the galaxy has retreated. The distance between us and it has increased by exactly the same distance. The chase is eternal and fruitless. The radiation never catches up with us and the galaxy remains invisible to our telescopes, optical and radio. The galaxies of the expanding universe move away and move faster until they attain the speed of light. Then they slip over the edge of space and time, vanishing from our sight forever.

It is a lucky thing for us that they do vanish and that their rays never reach us. Individually, distant galaxies send very little light to the earth. But there are so many of them that the total radiation from all the galaxies in a universe without an edge, an infinite universe, would be enormous. If their collective light reached us, we would have no nights. The skies would always and everywhere be blazing with a light equivalent to that of the sun. Life would not exist on earth or anywhere else, because of the lethal radiation. The heat of the galaxies would burn everything to a crisp. But we do not receive light from an infinite number of galaxies. Many, many galaxies have traveled beyond the point of no return, beyond the point where their radiation can reach us. They have vanished as the universe inflates. In other words, the skies are dark at night because the universe is expanding.

This expansion also sets a theoretical limit to our observations. Imagine a future radio telescope with a range of ten billion light-years, and hooked up to a large television screen. We see images at one, two, three, nearly four billion light-years. Beyond that, however, we see nothing. The screen is dark. We are looking at the edge of the observable part of the universe. We know, or at least our theories tell us, that somewhere in the blackness uncounted galaxies are speeding away through space. Perhaps we see a galaxy moving through the limits, half visible and half invisible, like a person passing out of a room. It is moving into an abyss whose depths we can never explore.

Thus radio astronomy may bring us to the end of observable space. We come to the ultimate frontier of our knowledge of the universe—unless, of course, we discover something unexpected. Man has lived through many advances which seemed impossible; he has surpassed many limits. The history of exploration is a long record of things that were not supposed to be done. There were oceans that could never be crossed and we have crossed them. We have scaled unscalable mountains, and fly daily and routinely through the sound barrier in the skies.

We should not believe too deeply in the limitations we conceive for ourselves. There may be similar breakthroughs in outer space, and radio astronomy may carry us through and over and beyond the very edges of the universe.

# INDEX

Absolute zero, 139
Absorbed waves, 190-194
Aerial, narrow-cone vs wide-cone, 43-44; *see also* Antenna; Interferometer; Searchlight aerial; Twin aerial
American Astronomical Society, 164, 193
American Telephone and Telegraph Company, 15
Ames, Adelaide, 125
Andromeda nebula, 20, 102, 108, 125, 177, 196; described, 117-118, 168; in "radio" light, 118; as seen in color television, 220
Antares, size of, 61
Antenna, coiled, 123-124; half-wave dipole, 42; *see also* Aerial
"Antenna farm," Ann Arbor, 122
Aquila, extra-intense signals from, 26
Armagh Observatory, Northern Ireland, 200
Asteroids, 201
Astronomy, historical nature of observations in, 96; radio, *see* Radio astronomy
*Astrophysical Journal*, 27, 101, 105, 192

"Atlas," rocket, 221
Atmosphere, earth's, 199; as barrier to radiation, 13; bulge in, 31; disturbances in, 8; radio "window" in, 14
Atom-smashing machine, University of California, 147-148
Atomic bomb, 148, 224
Atomic Energy Commission, 150
Atomic particles, oscillation of, 12; in sun's chromosphere, 66
Atomic power, and radio stars, 150-152
Aurora, 84-85; *see also* Northern Lights
Australia, Radio Physics Laboratory (Sydney), 33; radio telescopes in, 47-48
Australian National University, 126

Baade, Walter, 95, 98, 102, 105, 107, 127, 231; discovers colliding galaxies in Cygnus, 109
Baldwin, John, 116
Bell Telephone Laboratories, Holmdel, N.J., 7, 30; press release on stellar radio waves, 15
Big Dipper, 26, 37

# ABOUT THE AUTHOR

JOHN PFEIFFER, author of *Science in Your Life* and *The Human Brain,* is one of the leading American science writers. After graduating from Yale in 1936, he went to work at *Newsweek* as science and medicine editor. Since then he has been science director of the Columbia Broadcasting System, where he did science-news network broadcasts and a series of twenty-six weekly dramatizations of science, and a member of the editorial board of *Scientific American.*

For the past five years he has worked as a free-lance writer. His articles have appeared in numerous magazines, including *This Week, Popular Science, The American Scholar, Coronet, Look, The New York Times Magazine, Maclean's, The Scientific Monthly* and *Science Digest.* He has also written motion-picture and television scripts, book reviews and special reports for industrial research laboratories.

The author is president of the National Association of Science Writers, an organization which has done much to raise standards of science reporting in the United States and—indirectly—throughout the world. The Guggenheim Foundation awarded him a fellowship to write *The Changing Universe,* and to visit laboratories in England and Holland as well as in the United States.

Mr. Pfeiffer does his writing in New Hope, Bucks County, Pennsylvania, where he lives with his wife and son.